CHARLOTTE and Dr. JAMES

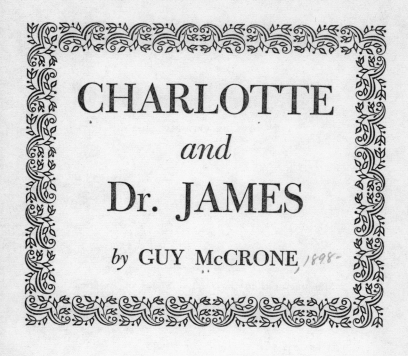

CHARLOTTE
and
Dr. JAMES

by GUY McCRONE

FARRAR, STRAUS & CUDAHY • *New York*

TO SCOTTISH READERS

No. Again no portraits. Least of all of
anyone now or ever attached to Glasgow University. I merely rolled down a
backcloth representing its august walls—
very much, really, as the Keswick photographer rolled down his backcloth of
the Lake of Como, when he took James'
and Charlotte's honeymoon photograph.

CHARLOTTE and Dr. JAMES

CHAPTER ONE

I

"Mrs. Raymond?"

"Margaret Raymond speaking."

"Lady Mennock's granddaughter?"

"Yes. Who are you, please?"

"I'm a nurse. I'm speaking from Scotland. Your grandmother asked me to telephone you."

"Nurse? Is my grandmother ill?"

"No, Mrs. Raymond." The voice was heavy with professional calm. "No. It's Sir James. Your grandfather fell down in his study this evening. So far as we can tell, he's paralyzed down one side and he doesn't seem able to speak. But his mind is clear. We asked him if he wanted you, and he nodded. *She* certainly does."

"Tell them I'll try to catch the early plane."

It was a brilliant morning in the beginning of September, as Margaret crossed with the other passengers to the waiting airplane. She felt tired, brittle and worried. She had slept very little. The telephone conversation had been going round in her head all night.

As she went up the metal steps and entered the sloping twilight, the carefully outlined lips of the air hostess said: "Good morning, Madam." Wanly, Margaret answered: "Good morning" and continued up the center passage in search of a window seat, a seat in which she could sit in comfort for the next two hours, dozing, looking out and trying not to feel too apprehensive.

The plane was almost full, but she found a seat in front, and was beginning the cramped and tilted battle of stowing coat, waterproof, last-minute package and handcase into the rack above her head, when she noticed a large, untidy young man, dressed in an old tweed jacket reinforced with leather at the cuffs and on the shoulders, where it was marked by the straps of a rucksack. He was coming up the passage towards her, peering shortsightedly to right and

[3]

left of him through very thick lenses, looking for an empty seat with the concentration of a field botanist in search of specimens.

Margaret hoped he would not take the empty place beside her. She could see one still unoccupied further down. He was such an odd-looking creature, with his untidy hair, his crumpled, dark blue shirt and his square face burnt to brick red by what had obviously been a walking holiday under a continental sun. And those glasses dehumanized him, somehow. They were so strong that, through them, his eyes looked like black beads surrounded by rings of silver. The Frog Footman came into her mind as she turned to go on with her struggles.

"Can I put these up for you?"

"Oh, thank you."

Yes. Here he was. And now there seemed so much of him that, sitting next to her, he would, she felt, be spilling his uncomfortable largeness over the center arm between them, taking all the floor space for his great feet, and bulging out beyond the back of his own seat with his massive shoulders.

But it didn't seem so bad now that they were settled down and were putting their seat belts about them. Indeed, the young man seemed to be trying so hard not to inconvenience her by placing his feet in the passage and keeping off the center arm, that she felt impelled to say: "Please, I've got all the room I need. Are you sure you've got all you want?"

"Oh, yes. Yes, quite enough, thank you." The sunburnt lips widened into a nervous, dazzling smile; dazzling in the sudden display of gleaming teeth.

But what an odd voice he had! Shy, prim and self-conscious, with an accent that could only belong to genteel Glasgow. An accent which, although it suited his startled expression, was uncomfortably imposed upon powerful resonances that should have belonged to a Russian bass.

The entrance door was slammed and the plane moved across to its place on the runway. Now for some minutes it stood, shuddering in the roar of its own propellers, then it ran forward, gaining speed, and rose up into the morning sunshine.

Margaret could see the new-built streets, squares and crescents of outer-fringe London tilt unnaturally towards her as they turned to fly north. She unloosened her seat belt, settled into her window corner and closed her eyes.

[4]

The young man beside her was glad of this; for now, without seeming to be impertinent, he would be able to study his neighbor as much as he liked. And he liked very much indeed, for the short-sighted eyes had read the luggage label dangling from her handcase.

"Mrs. Donald Raymond." But he hardly needed the label. Could anyone mistake the family likeness?

Behind her closed eyes, Margaret had no idea of the intense interest, the veneration her mere presence was evoking; veneration to the point of idolatry for a great surgeon and a great teacher. The young man had sat at Sir James Mennock's feet.

And this was the old man's granddaughter! She had Mennock written all over her. And yet, now that he came to look at her, wherein did the likeness lie? Everywhere and nowhere. The old man's lean face had distinction, but it was large-featured and deeply lined. This young woman's features were small and her skin was fine and had that transparency which goes sometimes with copper-red hair. But these closed eyes were set like his. And her attitude, the way in which, now at this moment, she lay back relaxed, her hands straight and crossed, one over the other, was Sir James all over again.

He bent forward a little to look at Margaret's hands. They were the comely hands of a young woman. That was all. Not the oddly long, surgeon's hands of the old man who was his idol. And yet, there she was, proclaiming herself a Mennock merely by the way she had crossed them.

Mrs. Donald Raymond. Now who had Donald Raymond been? Yes. A journalist. A war correspondent? He could remember the name Donald Raymond at the head of war dispatches. Raymond couldn't have been married to this girl when he was writing these. Margaret's neighbor sat back. Everything connected with a Mennock held a fascination for him. Been?

Yes. This young woman's husband was dead. For more than a year now, he reckoned. Perhaps two. He couldn't be sure. She must have been married for only a short time. Then there had been an accident. A street accident, wasn't it? Now it came to him how Sir James, much distressed, had mentioned it one morning; and how, in a tongue-tied way, he had said he was sorry and that he had noticed the death in the newspaper. Remembering unhappily how futile, somehow, his attempts at respectful condolence had sounded to himself, the young man took off his thick spectacles, polished them with the thoroughness of strong emotion, and put them back on his nose.

For a time he sat, looking more startled than ever, deploring his shyness, his own absurd futility, his lack of poise. Far less brilliant people had passed him on the climb upwards, merely because they could bestow the right smiles and the right words in the right places at the right moments. It had even cost him something to say, a few minutes ago: "Can I put these up for you?" to this young woman beside him!

But his intense interest in Mrs. Raymond would not allow him to linger over his own disabilities. This girl must have been very young when her husband was killed. She didn't look more than twenty-five now. Poor thing! She looked so frail and elegant there by the window with her eyes closed! Surely any man would be glad— Now, if he— But this miserable shyness of his had always— And, of course, the Mennocks were bigwigs.

"Coffee?" The outlined lips were bending, amiable and inviting, over a tray bearing plastic cups filled with a brown liquid.

III

Margaret opened her eyes a little resentfully. The hypnotic throb of the propellers and the pleasant warmth of the plane had brought her gratefully to the edge of sleep. But now, collecting her wits, she accepted a cup from the large male hand that passed it to her, refusing sugar but stirring it dreamily while she looked through the window.

It was a perfect morning. The sky outside was cloudless. Far below she could see thin mists veiling, here and there, low riverside meadows that lay still shaded from the early, slanting sunlight. Cattle were grazing diligently in the day's first freshness. Blue wisps of smoke rose straight up from red-tiled farmsteads. Fields of ripening grain patched the earth with gold. The countryside near Glasgow, she reflected, would be coming into its autumn glory.

Glasgow. Her grandfather. Apprehension was back, stabbing at her vitals. Margaret swallowed down her coffee in quick gulps, gave back the empty cup to her obliging neighbor, thanked him for disposing of it, wondered for a flickering instant if he were on the point of trying to open a conversation, decided that it was impossible to

[6]

tell what was going on behind those spectacles and once again lay back in her corner, crossing her hands, closing her eyes, and giving herself up to thinking of her grandparents, James and Charlotte Mennock.

Poor granny! How would she take this illness? The old people were so utterly bound up, one in the other. Now Margaret could see her lying on the familiar sofa at the foot of her grandfather's bed. On sunny afternoons his room, high up at the top of the house, was her favorite place of retreat. Her own room next to it only got the morning sunshine. It was to his that she came to read or rest. Sometimes, when he had leisure, they would both be there, he in his deep chair, his long legs in front of him; each of them silent and content merely to exist together.

An old memory came back to Margaret; how as a little girl she had sometimes resented this oneness. How she had felt a sense of exclusion. But that was nothing; the mere childish jealousy of a little creature to whom they had been the center of the universe. Her parents in everything, indeed, but fact.

The propellers hummed steadily. Above them she could hear the voices of other passengers as they sat talking together. Someone was smoking a cigar. Margaret changed her position to one still more comfortable and let her thoughts run on.

How strange it was that she had never quite seen her grandparents as individuals, as a man and a woman living out their own lives! Or was it not strange? Didn't all children do this with their close familiars? But now she was no longer a child. She was twenty-six. She had loved a man, married him and lost him. It was time, surely, for her to see them with adult eyes.

James Mennock had been a raw medical graduate from Ayrshire when he had come to know Charlotte Gailes. She was only sixteen. They claimed to have met each other at the Glasgow Exhibition of 1901. That, at any rate, was part of the family story. But Charlotte was the only child of a professor of Glasgow University—and professors were professors in those days, Margaret had been given to understand—and her mother was the daughter of a rich shipowner. Such people couldn't have wanted this young countryman as a son-in-law. Besides, though age and honors had given him distinction, young James Mennock with his red hair and his large bones could never have been handsome. What had brought about this marriage? How did it come to be allowed?

[7]

Now she was half aware of the plane swaying a little, rocking like a boat on a gentle sea. With this movement the propellers changed tune for a time, then they settled down once again into their steady drone. People were still talking quietly. She still smelt the cigar faintly. Pictures of her childhood, of her Glasgow surroundings, rose and changed in her mind. And questions.

Her father? The father she had never been old enough to know. To her very young self, the words "father" and "mother" had meant two photographs on her bedroom mantelpiece, that her sentimental grandmother had, now and then, required her to kiss.

But to her grandparents, her father must have been very real indeed. Yet why had they said so little about him? Or had it been herself who had been without curiosity? It was queer to think of James and Charlotte Mennock with a son of their own. Queer to think of them ever being real parents. And had they treated this boy as gently as they had treated the boy's daughter? Or had they been overanxiously stern with him? And how and where had her father met her mother? Why hadn't she heard about that either. Questions.

But now Margaret began to feel a pressure in her ears. She opened her eyes and was surprised to see the seat belt warning. She had felt no sense of passing time. She must have been almost asleep as she lay back, allowing these thoughts to take shape. She looked from the window. Yes. They were coming in. Running up to the heart of the city in order to take the Renfrew runway pointing towards its western end.

There was a mid-Victorian picture map of Glasgow hanging in her grandfather's study. The town down there looked like it now. The Clyde and the bridges. But steamers. Not the clippers with their tall masts as in the picture. The Merchants' House steeple. And the cathedral up there in the distance.

The plane was turning, dropping low over the rooftops on this fine morning. Port Dundas over there. The River Kelvin. This Glasgow-bred girl felt excitement at seeing these familiar things thus unfamiliarly. Hillhead and her grandparents' house. He was down there! Again apprehension stabbed. Poignant and unbearable this time. Was he still alive? How had he passed the night? Now they were over the university buildings. On a level, almost, with its high, fretted spire. Partick. The Clyde again. Flowing broader now, between suburbs, shipyards and open green fields. The distant outline of Renfrew steeple.

They touched down. And, as the London plane ran forward and came to a standstill, her neighbor sprang to his feet, brought down her belongings, received a stranger's thanks and turned away.

Margaret, fully awake now, crowded with the others down to the entrance door and stepped out into the light of the mid-morning.

CHAPTER TWO

I

It was Sunday, a fortnight later.

Sir James Mennock, as he emerged from sleep, heard the university chimes sound all the quarters; then, after an interval, ponderously strike four. For a time he continued with his eyes shut, listening to the other sounds of the September afternoon. Through the open window of his top floor bedroom, he could hear a light breeze catch the treetops, rustling the leaves and causing the birds to flutter and chirp among the branches. From across the road there came, now and then, bursts of church music. The organist must be practicing for the evening service. Footsteps on the pavement outside. Children's voices. The churning of gears, as a town bus ascended University Avenue. The rush of cars speeding over the hill past the university gates. Sounds from his own familiar, cheerful world.

Sir James did not move. He stayed propped up in the position in which he had dozed off, his lean face still pink from sleep, his thick hair as white, almost, as the pillows that supported him. He felt placid and content. Content still to be alive, to be free of pain, to know that, for this time at least, he had been given a reprieve. Being among the first surgeons of his country, he had of course no delusions about his condition. This, as he had explained to his granddaughter Margaret, was the first ringing of the bell. He must now, he supposed, consider his life's work as finished. But the bell need not ring again for a year or two and there was, as he had put it, plenty of him left to keep him happy. His mind, he was thankful to say, was clear. And his speech had come back very quickly. What damage the attack had done to his ability to move about was not yet defined. But whatever it might be, he was ready, he told himself, to accept it. There would now be leisure to read the books he had not had time to read; to write a bit, perhaps, or at least to arrange for publication what was of use among his still unpublished papers.

A light clearing of the throat and the rustle of a turned page reminded him that his wife, having taken the nurse's place for a time, was there, reading by the window. He moved on his pillow a little, clasped his hands in front of him—the long, clever hands that were a source of Mennock vanity and student admiration—then he opened his eyes.

"James! I didn't know you were awake!"

He looked at her. "And what would you have done if you *had?* Treated me to a step dance?"

"I might. You never know." As she got up, Lady Mennock pointed one toe. "No. I was thinking of tea, of course. I'll plug in the kettle. What a perfect day it is!" She made the connection, smiling to herself, pleased at this sign of his betterment, then she stood for a time admiring the September afternoon from the open window.

Her husband lay watching her. It was difficult to think of Charlotte as a woman of seventy. She was still tall and slender and looked not more than sixty. She had always been pretty rather than beautiful. Certainly never regal, as her mother had been. And she had retained her youthful habit of cheerfulness, of quick response to gaiety; qualities that came from an age of innocence, he supposed, yet could not be called either idiotic or kittenish. The young women of these present days of beauty parlor charm didn't seem to have them; which was, now that he came to think of it, a pity.

But this brought his granddaughter to his mind. "Where's Maggs?" he asked, using his own pet name for Margaret.

Lady Mennock turned from the window and began to busy herself with the tea things. "I told her to get the car and drive out into the country somewhere and give Macpherson a run. He was sitting at the front door, begging to be taken. It seemed ridiculous for her to be in on an afternoon like this. I suggested she might get in touch with some of her old friends. But she didn't seem to want to."

"What way that?" With his intimates, and especially since he had grown older, Sir James fell back now and then upon the accents and turns of speech of his Ayrshire boyhood. Indeed, it had become an affectation with him.

"My dear, I can't tell you!" Charlotte stood still for a moment thinking, then added: "You know, James, Margaret is different from what she used to be."

"Different?"

"Well, older. I don't know. Strung up. But different anyway. Different in her ways. Now that you're better and able to talk to her, you'll see what I mean."

"She canna very well help being different, can she? What with losing young Raymond and all the rest of it."

"I still can't understand why she didn't come back to live with us after Donald was killed."

Sir James's quicker understanding could think of all kinds of reasons. The grim independence of bereavement for one. But he merely said: "She would have her own notions, I daresay. Has she spoken about going back to London?"

"Not exactly. But I know she means to go." Charlotte spooned dry tea into the teapot. "I wish she would stay with us, James. Can't we do something to persuade her? I detest the thought of losing her again. Besides the child needs feeding and looking after. They don't take time to eat properly in London. I don't suppose it would be right to suggest that it's her duty to stay with us? I suppose that would be much too selfish, or old-fashioned or something?"

"She hasna gone back yet," was her husband's dry comment.

II

Margaret felt grateful to her grandmother for having turned her out of doors on this fine Sunday afternoon as, from the hill above Milngavie, the full glory of the western mountains broke suddenly upon her. She felt she must stop for a moment. She had forgotten about this in the years she had been in London.

As her grandfather's old car, large and dignified and professional, came smoothly to a standstill the white Skye terrier beside her, now looking to be set free, began to give little, glad yelps, pattering about on the leather seat in an ecstasy of anticipation. She put out a hand to calm him. "Not yet, Macpherson. We're not getting out yet."

With one hand on the dog's rough head, Margaret continued for a moment to look about her. At the nearby moors, blowing with bracken. At the Campsie Fells, there across the Blane Valley; a long wall of green velvet. At the valley itself, lying remote and veiled, a little, in a golden afternoon haze, cradling in its middle distance woodlands and broken tree-clad knolls. At the farther distance, where the sweep of the valley flattened out towards Loch Lomond. At the hill of Dungoyne and then across open country to Ben Lomond itself, standing up in front of other, remoter peaks; blue, receding wraiths on a jagged skyline.

For a time Margaret stayed, wondering, grateful merely to be up here. But presently Macpherson's impatience brought her back and she released the brakes, letting the car slide forward down the hill.

And now, as she turned east along the Blane Valley, it came to her that her return to Scotland, to this countryside, to that old terrace house up there near the university, was working a change within her. What change?

Until this afternoon she had scarcely thought about herself. There had been others to think about. Her grandmother. The climate of anxiety in a house of critical illness. The sight of her grandfather's distresses in the first days of her coming. The uncertainty whether he would live, and if so, whether life would henceforth merely be a weight upon him.

These had been weeks of tension. But the old man had begun to improve. Everyone could breathe once more and the house was settling back, finding its calm routine.

Having driven some miles under high trees and by the rich farmlands of the valley, Margaret found herself at the Cross of Lennoxtown. There, following an instinct, she turned from the main road, taking the one that climbs north through a high fold in the wall of the Campsies. For a time it rises straight and unvaried, a long diagonal on the green hillside. Where it turns at length to lose itself in the hills, she left the car and, following the little terrier, jumping and barking with delight, gave herself to the stiff half hour climb which leads to the first hilltop above the precipices.

In the old days this had been a favorite scramble; and now, as she labored upwards, she found herself regretting, a little, the schoolgirl who had come up here so easily. Yet presently, others, as they bade good day to the hatless young woman sitting there on the cairn of stones that marks the summit, could not easily have told whether the owner of that copper hair and that flushed face was twenty-six or sixteen.

Again she slid a caressing hand down the white back of Macpherson, who now sat close beside her with his tongue hanging out, breathless like herself and sharing their joint achievement.

What had brought her back up here? She could have given no reason. Was she looking for something?

It might be. For she had come up here with Donald Raymond

[13]

two days before they were married. "Take me away from all the fuss, Margaret!" And they had escaped and climbed to this high place.

Donald. Whatever had prompted her to climb to these bleak moors, it was memory that she found there. Memory that rose, suddenly, to stab her like a knife. Now the grey roofs of Lennoxtown, far below the autumn valley, the wooded hills, the distant smoke cloud which was Glasgow, swam before her.

Donald. They had sat up here, talking of their plans. Confident, happy, curious, each about the other, full of high hope, very much in love. Another young man and his girl setting out to show the world that they were, as Donald had put it, going to make a go of it.

And for a time they had done so. If making a go was leading a busy life of noisy high spirits, of having to see, to know, to talk about everything; the life of an alert young couple with many friends. And for his sake she had flung herself into it. Even learning to type and take notes so that she might be useful to him in his work; even, with his guidance, writing a magazine story or two, just because he kept insisting that she could.

And at the core and center of it all there had been Donald. Donald her lover. Who remained behind with her, there in the darkness, after the noise of the day was over and everyone else was gone.

A light breeze ran across the hills, rustling the dry grasses. Somewhere a curlew rose, repeating its unhappy cry. Down below, a car could be heard climbing up the hill road by which she herself had come. Macpherson was now on the edge of the cliff barking at the noise it was making. But Margaret neither heard nor noticed.

And then there had been no Donald. A policeman at the door. An hysterical visit to a mortuary. A dead man. Collapse, and the loss of the child they had expected. Her illness. The grandparents in London. Darkness and bitterness for a young woman who had everything one moment, and nothing the next.

Stung by memory, Margaret had sprung to her feet and was blindly pacing along the hilltops. In time the effort brought her to her senses. She was dismayed and angry. Angry at letting self-pity slip its chains. Friends had praised her for her pluck. Pluck? What kind of pluck was this? These things had happened nearly two years ago. She had, she told herself, long since won such battles; had thrust behind her these sudden storms of remembering; had fought her way back. She had better not come up here again if this was what the place did to her!

Plunging angrily among rank tufts of grass and across squelching peat flats, Margaret took herself to task. Less than an hour ago, she reminded herself, she had felt at peace! There, on the hill with the western highlands spread before her! Now this shameless letting go!

She halted, dried her eyes and looked about her. High clouds were coming over now. In the distance she could see the white spot which was Macpherson plunging in the grasses, disappearing into, and reappearing out of peatholes, as he set up the peewits that came flying and complaining over her head, balancing and wheeling in the growing strength of the breeze.

Margaret stood still, glad to feel the cool air upon her face; glad to feel that the foe was once again in retreat, that another fight was won.

Calling to Macpherson, she turned and made her way back down-hill.

III

"Good morning, Grandfather."

"Come in, Maggs, come in." He lay against his pillows, breakfasted, washed, shaved and ready to face his day.

"You're looking much better," Margaret said.

"Glad to hear it. Sit down and talk."

She smiled. To be told to sit down and talk had meant, in the old days, that he was determined to find out something. "Are you sure talking is allowed?" she asked, teasing him a little.

"Sit down when you're told!"

She laughed. It was an old habit, this striking of sparks, each from the other.

Sir James lay watching her as she perched on the arm of his fireside chair. Charlotte was right. Margaret had changed. And not for the better, he felt. She looked thin, tense and too alert. Maturity and loss had left their mark, refining her face, perhaps, but giving it an air of sophistication that was unfamiliar to him. What kind of person had his granddaughter become?

"Well, darling? Why these consulting-room eyes?"

"And what about you?" he asked abruptly.

"Me, Grandfather? Well, what about me?"

[15]

"Your Granny says you're needing looking after."

"Granny likes to make fusses."

He noted the nervous, impatient movement. "Are you going to stay with us this winter?"

As he had intended, she was a little surprised by this question. "Are you sure you really want me?"

"Your Granny would like you to stay."

"And what about you?"

"I daresay I could put up with you." He watched her, assessing her as she smiled at this then got up abruptly and began to walk about.

"I don't know. I must think. I've got so many friends in London now."

What sort of friends, he wondered? Was his granddaughter, having been left with enough money to keep her idle, allowing herself to become a smart nobody? She was too intelligent for that. "Unsettled?" he asked.

She nodded.

He stretched out a hand and she came to him, responding to an old habit. Often, as a little girl, she had stood thus close beside his chair, her hand in his own. "Missing Donald, still?"

Again she nodded.

"Nobody else?"

She shook her head with emphasis.

These gestures from her childhood pleased him. They told him he could still talk to her. "You're restless, Maggs."

"I'll stay as long as you need me," she said.

"But not any longer?"

That she did not answer was answer enough. But he ventured: "Looking for a job or something?"

"I'm not sure. No. Not particularly."

He had been able, he told himself, to patch up the body better than most; but the patching up of the mind had not been in his line of business. "What do you do with your time in London?" he asked, caressing the hand he held.

"Go about, I suppose. Amuse myself."

No. She was worth more than that. "No special interest?"

"Nothing much, really."

This indifferent creature was not his eager grandchild. What must

[16]

he do to bring her back? "What kind of life did you lead down there when Donald was alive?"

She turned to look down at him. "With Donald? Everything was different. Everything was—" she finished with a shrug.

"You helped him with his work, I've heard tell?"

"Well, I learned to type and helped with letters and things. He was teaching me to write stories. I actually sold one or two."

"No interest in that? Never thought of trying again?"

Yet once again the headshake. "It might bring back too much." Her expression was defensively bright.

He dropped her hand, allowing her to move away from him, and lay back among his pillows. No. This was not the old Margaret. She had, he knew, shown courage. But loss had left a numbness of the spirit. How was he to help her?

This was his dead son's daughter. He had failed the boy in the moment of his need. Must he fail the boy's daughter too?

He was an old man now, and ill. But time to think lay lavish on his hands. He must do what he could.

She saw he was perplexed and was touched by it. "Darling! If you're going to worry about me like this, the sooner I go away again the better. I'm really all right! I swear it!" She crossed to his bedside, kissed him lightly on the brow and left him.

CHAPTER THREE

I

Coming into her drawing room that afternoon Lady Mennock found Margaret squatting on the floor before an open cupboard, having taken an album of family photographs from a lower shelf. "Whyever are you looking at these old things?" she asked.

"I wanted to see what you and Grandfather looked like when you were young."

"But you've seen these often before, Margaret."

"Not for a long time."

"And why now?"

The young woman on the floor raised her eyes. "I happened to be thinking about you, that's all."

"Stand up and let me have a look too. I'll tell you about them."

Margaret did not want, particularly, to be told about them. She had wanted to bring these pictures to life for herself, to examine them in the light of her own rather aimless curiosity. Besides, the old people's memories and descriptions could seem so irrelevant sometimes. So little to the point. She struggled obediently to her feet, however, holding open the heavy book, musty, padded and gold-embossed, for her grandmother to see.

"I remembered there was this photograph of you and Grandfather on the day of your wedding."

They stood together, looking at the picture of a woman, sweet, solemn and very young, in the clothes of the early nineteen hundreds, standing stiff and staring, beside a yet more stiff and staring young man in a country-cut suit, a large young man with a rough-hewn, self-confident face and a mop of thick hair.

"Keswick? Why Keswick?" Margaret asked, turning. The card had moved in the album, revealing the name and address of the photographer.

Surprisingly, Lady Mennock colored and looked confused. "Yes," she said. "We ended up at Keswick. No. That wasn't taken on the day of our wedding. It was taken a day later."

Margaret had, as her grandmother said, looked at this old photograph many times. But never before with the eyes of adult curiosity. Why had she never before required herself to breathe life into these waxwork figures? To feel that in the next instant the photographer would replace the cap on the lens of his concertina camera, say perhaps: "That will do now, thank you. It should look very nice, I think," help the young lady, perhaps, to disentangle her veil from the iron clamp that had been holding her head steady; warn her husband, perhaps, not to lean back too heavily on the plaster parapet overlooking the Lake of Como, and bow them out? Never before required herself to picture this young man and woman warmly arm in arm now, and not in the least frozen as they were in the photograph, going off down the street happily—perhaps still tremulously—preoccupied by the new relationship into which they had just entered, each with the other; preoccupied by their new-found feelings, their new-found obligations and their hopes?

And yet, didn't most young people find it difficult to believe that a strong passion, personal and obsessive, could ever have taken hold of their elders? The very look of the clothes in these old photographs seemed to prevent such a belief somehow. It was possible to think of them as kind, loving and protective; or stern and disciplinarian. But was it possible that these jackets, square and high-lapelled, these stovepipe trousers, these waspwaists, that looped and fringed upholstery, could ever have housed the fires and flutterings, the agencies and raptures, which the contents of that extraordinary clothing had indeed handed down to the descendants who were asking this very question?

"That was a nice dress," Lady Mennock was saying. "I had chosen it with my mother, your great-grandmother, Margaret, in the autumn before. But it was still almost new and did very well. Bottle green, it was, and the very best material. I remember I got it dreadfully stained with mud one morning on a long walk that ended by our having to go through fields. I didn't know what to do! But in the end I thought of a plan! I told our landlady I was tired and having the afternoon in bed, wrapped the dress in brown paper, and made your grandfather march off with it under his arm to a tailor! He was a little shocked at my untruthfulness, but he brought it back before long looking just like new!"

[19]

Margaret laughed at this; although at once it raised questions. It gave her a pleasant glimpse of these two as they must have been then, young and silly, and somehow a little touching. But why one dress? Why her grandfather with that brown paper parcel under his arm? Had she no other dresses with her? Why only a landlady? Keswick must have had good hotels by then, surely? "You make yourselves sound just like a little runaway couple!" She spoke, expecting the immediate and quite simple explanation of an innocent mystery. But now Lady Mennock's face looked vague and distressed; beset, it seemed, by unnamed scruples.

Her granddaughter's curiosity increased. "Oh, Granny!" she cried. "You must tell me! You don't say you *were!*"

The old woman turned away from her. "Well, I suppose so. In a sense."

"You suppose? But you must have been or not been! People can't run away 'in a sense'!"

"Well, at any rate by then they knew where we had gone." But now Lady Mennock's manner became a little firm. "Margaret, don't ask me any more. I shouldn't have been so talkative just now."

"But Granny, dearest! It's the first time I've heard of all this! Can't you see how curious it makes me? After all, I *am* a direct result!"

"No, please!" Lady Mennock stopped for a moment, then added in a low whisper as though to reassure herself: "It was all forgiven, of course. But I've never wanted to talk about it."

This was bewildering. Bewildering to be met by this unusual firmness. Bewildering to have the portcullis of a Victorian upbringing suddenly dropped in front of her face. Margaret tried a last rattle at the bars. "But if whoever they were forgave you, why should you mind?"

"The fact remains that I do." Lady Mennock took the album from her granddaughter's hands and closed it. "Put that back in its place," she said quietly and went out of the room.

But of course Margaret took it up again and examined the two young faces closely. Did she now detect a sense of strain? Was there a look of defiance in her grandfather's staring expression? A look of fearfulness in her grandmother's? Or was her increasing curiosity prompting her to read what was not there?

She turned to the well-known Sargent portrait of her great-grandmother Mackinnon Gailes hanging solitary in its usual place of honor; a whole wall of the room given up to it. The American painter had not minimized the proud self-confidence, the look almost of arrogance, any more than he had minimized the elegance, the regal bearing, as she stood, ready, it seemed, to judge the world around her. Margaret had always been told the woman up there was sweet and lovable. Now she wondered. Had her grandparents been forced, in the end, to go to this woman and beg her forgiveness? And how had she taken it? And what of her husband, the old professor?

Their descendant began to feel she must find out what had happened.

II

After more than fifty years of marriage, there was little that Charlotte Mennock could conceal from her husband. Thus, as she came into his room, it was easy for Sir James to see that something had disturbed her. For a time he lay silent, watching her as she settled down in her chair by the open window, took up some mending and began to stitch busily. But even the very busyness of her fingers as she bent over her work told him that something had displeased her. "Well, Charlotte?"

She looked up, smiling, as though to reassure him that everything was as usual with her. "Well, James?"

"What's the trouble?"

"Trouble, James? What kind of trouble?" She bent over her work again.

"You werena pleased when you came in here just now."

"Oh, it was nothing. Something quite foolish." But it would come now, he knew. She could not keep things from him.

Presently Lady Mennock dropped her hands and turned for a moment to watch the light shower of rain that had begun to fall upon the leaves of the treetop outside the window. "No, it was nothing really," she said, turning back slowly. "I found Margaret looking at some of the old photographs just now, and very stupidly I allowed myself to be made cross by the questions she asked me."

"What photographs? And what questions?"

"Oh, she was looking at the old Keswick photograph and began cross-questioning me about it. I didn't like it. That was all."

Her husband chuckled. "And what way did you not like it?"

Charlotte's soft features took on a look of annoyance. "You know

[21]

perfectly well why I didn't like it, James! Just as well as I do! All that is better forgotten."

The old man lay back smiling to himself. At his wife's innocent indignation with their granddaughter. At the continuing freshness of her feelings. "What did Maggs want to know?" he asked presently.

"All kinds of questions about our marriage. I've never known her inquisitive like this before. She used to accept everything we told her."

"She's a grown woman now."

"That may be, James. But surely there are *some* things we are entitled to keep to ourselves."

"Did you tell her what happened?"

"No! Certainly not!"

Again he chuckled. It was a long time since he had seen so much spirit. It reminded him of the young Charlotte.

His amusement annoyed her. "It's all very well, James," she said picking up her sewing and reattacking it. "But I, at any rate, have no intention of pandering her curiosity! And why this eagerness? Besides, it wasn't your parents that we hurt."

Sir James made no reply to this. Nor did she seem to expect it. She had settled down to her work now, stitching diligently and in silence. Outside, the autumn rain became heavier, pattering noisily on the leaves. His bedside clock ticked steadily. Why should Maggs be eager?

Eager? The points of his long fingers came together as he lay thinking. The girl had seemed incapable of eagerness this morning. It had been as though a spring were broken in her. Since she had left him he had lain considering her as a case, worried and wondering. But now this. Even a new-found interest in themselves, her grandparents, might help. And, now that he came to think of it, there was much that he could do. There were old papers, diaries.

James looked at Charlotte. She was still working busily. The cloud had passed and her face was soft and gentle. Should he talk to her? Ask her what she thought of this? He knew that sympathy was his wife's quickest emotion. That there was nothing she would not do for her granddaughter. Even to allowing what she called "revelations."

The old man turned to speak, then thought better of it. No. Perhaps after all there was nothing in this idea. He had better wait and see.

[22]

But he did not have to wait for long. Next day, after bidding him good morning, Margaret at once asked: "Did Granny tell you we were looking at photographs yesterday?"

"She did." Sir James had not been prepared for this question. Yet it pleased, even excited him a little. He lay now, clasping and unclasping his hands, the ghost of a smile flickering. She had opened up the way. He must lead her in the direction he wanted her to take. "And what ones would you be looking at, Maggs?"

"The early ones. The one you had taken at Keswick at the time of your wedding, for instance. Granny began to tell me about it. Then, when she had made me thoroughly curious, she wouldn't tell me any more."

Sir James laughed. He was pleased to see the animation in her face. "And did you think you had descended from a very handsome couple?"

"Very. Were you terribly in love, Grandfather?"

"We wouldna be made of sawdust, likely enough."

"Oh, Grandfather," Margaret burst out, "do tell me about yourselves at that time!"

"Why?"

"Why not? I'm your own flesh and blood! Granny talked yesterday as if your marriage had been a scarlet sin!"

Again he laughed. "And do you believe your Granny could ever be a party to a scarlet sin?"

"No. Not even a pale pink one!"

"Oh, I wouldna just say that!"

"Well, then?"

Her grandfather looked before him thoughtfully. "Charlotte has always been far too anxious to spare other folk's feelings." He was speaking to himself, it seemed, naming as he now did, his wife by her name. "She certainly was then," he added, his mind apparently far away from his granddaughter. Margaret knew this to be a trick of his. A mannerism he had used with much effect, she had been told in professional consultation, if he wanted to consider, then to pounce. But now she was in hopes of hearing the Keswick story and sat waiting for it.

Instead he suddenly came out of his seeming reverie, looked at her and said: "Maggs, I wonder if you'll do something for me?"

"What do you want me to do, Grandfather?"

"You said you had helped your man in a secretarial way."

"Yes. But what—"

"Well, you can help me."

"But you *have* a secretary. What about Miss McQueen?"

Miss McQueen was a bulky lady in her middle fifties who puffed her discreet way upstairs of a morning, now that he was fit to receive her, went through his letters with him, took his instructions, then puffed downstairs again and out at the front door, the pages of her shorthand pad filled with his replies. These she typed with great perfection at Sir James Mennock's consulting rooms in Woodside Terrace near Charing Cross.

"It has nothing to do with Miss McQueen. It's personal stuff. Private papers. Letters. Diaries. If you've any curiosity about the Mennock or the Mackinnon Gailes families, you should get it satisfied there. You see, Maggs, when I thought I was going, two or three weeks since, I remembered and I was worried. There are boxes of these things in the basement storeroom at Woodside Terrace. They were brought from the country when we sold Brackencraigs House, and left at Charing Cross for want of anywhere else to put them. There must be papers of mine, of your own father's or your grandmother's. Things that strangers should never see. I want most of this burnt. But they had better be looked through first. You can take notes, if you think it is worth while. Will you do that for me?"

Margaret did not answer at once. She sat thinking. But presently she looked up. "Family secrets? Skeletons in the Mennock cupboard?"

He did not reply to this. He merely lay watching her.

"May I look in at your rooms first?" she asked.

He nodded. "Miss McQueen will light up the basement for you. I'll tell her you're coming."

CHAPTER FOUR

I

Miss McQueen's manner and bearing were nothing if not professional. Never for a moment did she allow it to be forgotten that she was the receptionist of an important surgeon. Sir James's rooms in Woodside Terrace were her kingdom. Here, in the somber dignity of what had once been the dining room and morning parlor of a large Victorian house, did Miss McQueen, her bulk enveloped in the whitest of outsize overalls, hold sway. Typing. Answering telephone inquiries. Making endless cups of tea for herself on a gas ring in the pantry. Opening the front door. All with an air of sympathy that was as deep as it was pessimistic. "Abandon hope all ye received by Miss McQueen!" the schoolgirl Margaret had once commented pertly. Her grandmother had asked her what she meant. But her grandfather had laughed.

As she admitted Margaret on the following day, Sir James's receptionist was quite as usual. "Good afternoon, Mrs. Raymond," she said in an asthmatic half whisper, pregnant with foreboding. "Sir James told me this morning that you mebbe might be coming. I said we would do everything we possibly could to help you." Apart from the royal "we," these words were straightforward enough. But their tone implied that Miss McQueen had already made all the professional arrangements for the removal of Margaret's entrails; that bravery was now the only thing left to Margaret; and that Miss McQueen knew just how Margaret was feeling and more than sympathized.

Her victim thanked her and followed her bulky whiteness across the checkered marble floor of the entrance hall.

"You'll be tired," Miss McQueen said, kind if illogical; taking it for granted that moving the body from one point to another must be as much of an undertaking for Mrs. Raymond as it was for herself.

"No. Not a bit. I've had a very pleasant walk across the park."

"Oh, well. I've just put on the kettle anyway. I'll show you where the boxes are. You'll have the keys? And then we'll have a nice cup of tea."

The storeroom in the basement was not so stark as Margaret had expected. It had been a maids' bedroom in the days when maids could be had in endless supply and could be stowed anywhere out of sight at such rare times as they were neither required to labor, nor linger, drilled and decorative, in pantries and front halls. There was a high, barred window, which could be opened to let in the air and some light, and an old-fashioned iron fireplace where a fire might still be lit. One side of the room was fitted with wooden racks upon which were set ten or twelve japanned deed boxes of the kind used in lawyers' offices. Miss McQueen's efficiency had of course seen to it that the place was clean. Upon a plain table set against another wall was a scatter of manuscript sheets and a reading lamp.

Margaret was surprised. "Do you work down here too sometimes?" she asked.

"No, Mrs. Raymond. You mean these papers? Oh, the doctor will have left them about, as usual! Sir James said the doctor was to get seeing all the old lecture notes and all the other things he wanted. I have the keys for *them*."

"Doctor? Doctor who?"

"Doctor Struan, Mrs. Raymond. He's worked a lot with Sir James. All last winter. He was helping Sir James with his book."

"Book? What book?"

"Some book he was helping Sir James with," Miss McQueen said, thus explaining fully.

"Does he come down here much?"

"Well, out and in; he's at the university."

"What does he do there?"

"Corpses."

"I see." Margaret steadied herself for an instant then asked: "Is he nice?"

Miss McQueen did not reply at once. She gave herself a moment in which to smolder, then answered: "Sir James thinks he's a paragon, anyway."

"Paragon? Paragon of what?"

"Oh, knowledge, I suppose," Miss McQueen spoke with resignation.

From this Margaret rightly concluded that the paragon did not stand high in Miss McQueen's estimation. "I must ask my grandfather to tell me about him," she said. "It's queer he hasn't."

"Remember Sir James has been very ill, Mrs. Raymond," Miss McQueen's voice was asthmatic now with devotion. The lightest criticism, except from herself, must not be allowed to touch Sir James. "These are his private boxes there. He's always kept the keys. I've never had them. Not that I would— Oh, I've quite enough responsibility already!"

"Of course you have, Miss McQueen!" Margaret hastened to say. "This is my grandfather's private bunch here. He says I am the first person he has ever given them to."

"Yes. These are his private keys. I've seen them often." Miss McQueen's voice was husky—with awe, Margaret hoped—as she added: "No, Mrs. Raymond. It's only for members of the family to touch these keys."

There was nothing to do but brush these words brightly aside. "Oh, I don't know, Miss McQueen! Now which would you say are the boxes he wants me to look at?"

"Sir James's private papers are in these here."

Since Miss McQueen's manner had become perhaps a little aloof, Margaret was not sorry that she whispered something about the kettle boiling in the pantry and took herself heavily up the basement stairs.

II

The three or four tin boxes on the shelf were heavy but easily accessible. She dragged them forward and by trial and error found the right keys, unlocking each in turn.

There were endless family letters, her grandparents', her father's, the letters of several hands she did not know; each carefully docketed with description and date by her grandfather. The look of these bundles touched Margaret with an odd excitement. Yet why throughout his life had a busy, brilliant man troubled to keep such things? To seek to preserve, in so far as he could, the memory of what was, after all, a family of no great importance? A last box, the largest and most solidly heavy, was packed with closely written diaries. This did not quite surprise her. How often had she been told in childhood "that Grandfather was writing his diary"? And, indeed, seen him at it? Once or twice she had meant to ask him what he did with them; where he put them as each year was finished. Here was the answer. As a child she had taken it for granted that her grandfather's diary-keeping was his hobby, a relaxation for his mind. And in this, perhaps, she had not been wrong.

Since they lay systematically, according to their years, Margaret, idly seeking a point of interest, easily found the diary written in the year of her birth and turned to the actual day, which was a Sunday. He had cut out and pasted in the announcement of the birth in the Glasgow *Herald* above his entry. Her feelings were strange as she read:

> At a Glasgow nursing home on 1st June, to Grace, wife of Alexander Henry Mennock, of Brackencraigs House, Loch Ard, Perthshire, a daughter.

And the entry beneath it. It was written at Brackencraigs House, James Mennock's country mansion.

> A perfect, early summer morning to welcome our granddaughter into God's world. A good omen, we must hope.
>
> The telephone by our bedside rang about six this morning. It is queer, now that I come to think of it, that habit did not even suggest to me this might be an emergency call for myself, breaking my week-end and calling me back to Glasgow. I knew before I lifted the receiver that the baby had been born. Not at all strange, of course, as the birth was overdue. And they had been told to telephone when things began to happen.
>
> We both got out of bed, put on dressing-gown and went to awaken Sandy. The boy was lying face down, half-uncovered, half tangled in bedclothes. He looked fifteen. I had to remind myself he was twenty-five and a married man. And now he is the father of a child! Young enough, at that, but there it is.

Margaret stopped for a moment to wonder. A difficult birth? Everyone anxious? Then why was her father out here with his parents by Loch Ard, thirty miles away from her mother? She read on.

> His mother roused him, then put her arms round him and told him he had a daughter. He looked dazed and pale, which was not surprising, considering how late and in what condition he had gone to bed. I told him I thought he should get up and go to Grace at once. He showed no slowness about this, I was glad to

see. As nobody in the kitchen was moving, his mother heated some coffee for him herself. I was also glad to see he was pleased and anxiously excited.

We stood, both of us, waving from the door as he drove round from the garage and away; both of us hoping, praying and feeling sentimental. At least I was. His mother was, of course, enjoying a good cry. "Stop yer greetin', Granny," I said, "and we'll go in and make some more coffee for ourselves." Which we did.

Since I wrote these last words, Sandy has telephoned. He sounded sensible and responsible and reported that Grace had a bad time but would be all right now. He is staying the night in Glasgow to be beside her. He told his mother, who took the receiver from me, that he has seen his daughter, refuses to consider her beautiful, but hopes for improvement later. Charlotte promised to visit the baby tomorrow when we get back.

Well, here we are, Charlotte and I with our first grandchild. It is a milestone. We are young grandparents. I am only fifty-one and she is forty-four! We might have had the child ourselves! But it is good that we are young. Sandy being Sandy. The baby may need us. Yet I hope everything will be better now. The boy has so much good in him. And I hope his daughter will bring it out.

Here the entry ended. Margaret laid down the diary. From the top of the stair, Miss McQueen's weak voice was calling that tea was ready. But she did not hear her.

"Sandy being Sandy?" But there were so many unanswered questions. Questions that would have answered themselves had she ever known her parents. She had been brought up by her grandmother to believe that they were perfect human beings and she had always accepted this. Now she must find out what kind of people they really were. But she must go carefully. And it was her grandfather she must ask. His judgments were much more robust, much less sentimental than the judgments of her grandmother. Lady Mennock was one of those who incline to practice charity at the expense of truth. But she, Margaret, must not risk upsetting the old man for a while. Memory might overexcite him and do him harm. She must wait.

But what sort of young man *was* her father then? She had always understood he was doing quite well in business; understood he had married a London girl who was an orphan; but that all was as it should be. But was it?

Now Margaret became aware of Miss McQueen standing in the doorway, a cup of tea in her hand, looking at her reproachfully.

"I thought mebbe that you didn't hear, Mrs. Raymond."

"Oh, Miss McQueen! I'm so sorry! But you shouldn't have troubled to bring this down. I could so easily—"

"There's sugar and milk in it," Miss McQueen said and, turning, retreated upstairs.

III

At random she now opened an early diary at an entry dated February, 1898, and written at Kinaldie, Ayrshire, where Sir James's father, old Peter Mennock, had been the village doctor. The writer must then have been a student, and was back at home with his father and his stepmother Constance Mennock.

Down for the weekend to see Father and Connie. Just had a blow-up because I wouldn't go with them to the Kirk. Connie's fault, of course. Father was far more reasonable before he married that daft swallow-the-poker from Glasgow. What he saw in her, God alone knows! And neither of them young, either. Love, if you are round about the fifties, must be a good lot blinder and a sight less particular than it is in the twenties, if you ask me!

Margaret laughed aloud at this. She had seen a photograph of Connie.

When the bells began to ring she came to ask me if I was all ready and I said I was damned if I was all ready so then she sent Father who said I was to come to please Mother because she was so proud of me and wanted to show me off when she had me at home and he knew I was tired but would I not just come?

Again Margaret laughed. This time at the boyish rage that had tumbled out with these words.

But he couldn't budge me and I have just had the great pleasure of seeing her flouncing out of the gate in her feather boa and white gloves dabbing her eyes with her genteel lace hanky. *After supper.* Have made my peace with Connie. Not because Father said any more. But because I took remorse of conscience. The poor body does her best. She can't help being what she is. She is not so bad. Although she made me angry again by saying in her hoity-toity way, that while of course, she forgave me, and knew I was a "splendid, clever boy" it would really pay me to master my quick temper, as it would count very much against me when "I came to make my way in this difficult, troubled world."

However, I held my tongue. And now that I come to think of it, of course the woman is right. I must improve my temper and my manners.

Went to evening service with them. Will be glad to get back to Glasgow tomorrow.

Sir James Mennock had come a long way since that entry, his granddaughter reflected. His quickness of temper had remained—Margaret had heard stories of nurses and housemen whom Sir James had found wanting—but ever since she had known him, it had been held on a tight rein and had seldom been shown to herself. Her grandmother must of course have done much with his manners.

Yet how oddly little she, Margaret, had thought about his early background, his father, his father's second wife, the Ayrshire village of Kinaldie. Here too she must find out more.

But time was running on. She had only meant to look in this afternoon. Unable to tear herself away just yet, however, she turned to another box and picked up a package of letters marked CHARLOTTE MACKINNON GAILES. She drew one out at random. It was from Lausanne in Switzerland and was dated mid-December, 1901. The handwriting was girlish and impetuous, but already recognizable as the hand of her grandmother.

MY DEAR DOCTOR JAMES,

The most *amazing thing* has happened! One of our girls has eloped! Yes! Here! Out of this pension! I still can't believe that I should ever have known and spoken to a girl who could do anything so exciting! Not that I know her very well. She was grown-up, eighteen at least, tall and fair, and *very* beautiful. She was a German called Hildegarde von Scharfenberg, and a baroness in her own right, whatever that means. Very aloof and passionate, but quite nice, really. She didn't speak much to anybody except to another German girl called Magdalene von Something Else, who is also a baroness and thinks her father once spoke to King Edward in Homburg, but is not quite sure.

Well, this morning they found a french window off the catch

and a girl's footprints in the snow! And then that Fraulein von Scharfenberg's bed had never been slept in! Isn't it lovely? And one of the maids declares that near the garden entrance a man's footprints met the girl's, and that the footprints went off through the gate together!

Where do you think they have gone? Italy, I feel. They *must* have gone to Italy. It is the only really romantic place! Venice! I think Lord Byron went to Venice.

We girls are supposed not to know anything about it. Mademoiselle Nantes told us at breakfast this morning that "dear" Hildegarde has suddenly been called home to Germany because of illness. We had to pretend to believe her, but of course we know all the time she was talking fiddle-de-dee. Besides, "dear" Hildegarde had confided in Magdalene, who told it as a great secret to the maid who saw the man's footsteps, who couldn't keep it to herself. So now we are all full of it, and can't think of anything else!

As I write this, a friend has just come in to tell me that Magdalene says the lover is a quite poor, but very handsome Italian, who was studying I don't know what here at the university. But Hildegarde is very rich, they say; castles and hunting boxes and everything. She will have more than enough money for two. So his poverty doesn't matter in the least. I *am* glad he is an Italian! Aren't you? And, they say, also, that she was *ruthlessly condemned by calculating parents* to marry a man she hated; a family connection or something, and quite old. Thirty, if he was a day! So really she had no choice. The engagement was to be announced whenever she got home in June. Can you blame the poor girl? *I* can't.

And now there is a rumour that her mother, the Countess von Scharfenberg, has been wired for. Another girl saw Mademoiselle, all worried and dressed up to go out, hurriedly writing on what looked like a telegraph form, then blotting it on a piece of blotting paper which the girl, of course, held up to a mirror the moment she had a chance. It wasn't clear but she thought it was the countess' name she read. I wonder if the countess will arrive all raging and fuming? What a fuss that will make! Poor Mademoiselle!

Your last letter arrived two days late. I don't know why. I was quite worried. They usually come so promptly. I am sorry to hear your father has been ill, but I hope it is a mere passing indisposition. *My* father and mother reappear in about a week's time, then we go on to Zurich for Christmas. But I've told you that before. Interesting; still I wish I were coming home, somehow.

Where do you think they will be now? My guess is: speeding towards sun-soaked Italy! I shall write again almost at once, of course, to keep you up to date.

Your stunned and excited friend,
CHARLOTTE GAILES

This letter delighted Margaret. She took it over to the work table and sat down to savor it. The young Charlotte must just have turned seventeen then. Wasn't she already too old to be scribbling such nonsense? Charlotte's granddaughter considered this. Charlotte was the only child of middle-aged parents, of course; adored, indulged and kept young for their amusement, probably. Indeed, Margaret herself had known something of this kind of upbringing. It had caused her too, she now reflected, to mature late. That must be the explanation. A long life had done much to change her grandmother. Yet there were echoes—irresponsibility, wilfulness—still quite recognizable in the old woman she knew.

What else? Was Charlotte in love with her James by this time? Hardly. Though she might imagine so. And being as she was, she would certainly consider it romantic to be already writing letters to a young man. Still, she was showing only a tepid regret at missing Christmas in Scotland.

But they seemed to exchange letters regularly, and already intimacy had reached the stage of her addressing him as her "dear Doctor James." Did her parents allow this? Or was it possible they knew nothing of it?

And young James? Why was he bothering to write? Didn't his Presbyterian conscience trouble him a little. Yet why should it, if Charlotte's parents knew? And these letters would amuse him. Did he keep corresponding merely to see what this absurd child would write next? Or could it be that he was flattered by the admiration of a professor's daughter? No. Not that. Margaret could not believe it had ever been in James Mennock's makeup to be flattered by social importance. Or was it possible that this brilliant young doctor could already be in love with a feather-brained schoolgirl? Margaret did not believe that either. She must ask her grandfather.

She got up and began putting everything back in place. No. On second thought she wouldn't ask. At any rate, not quite at once. The years played tricks with memory. Independently she would try to follow a thread through these papers. After that she would ask her grandparents to fill in the gaps in the story.

Story? Margaret continued to sit, pondering and fascinated. Should she try to set down some kind of—what?—narrative? Continuous record of these two people? Why not? And what kind of record? She must think about that too. But the idea began to take hold of her.

There was a nip of frost in the air and street lamps were coming to life as Margaret walked back, absorbed and, though she was not yet conscious of it, happy. Happy because the urge to write again possessed her. Hadn't Donald told her she could? Why not piece together the story of these two young people in the Keswick photograph and try to set it down?

IV

"Well, Maggs? Been at Woodside Terrace?" Sir James, who had been awaiting her return, watched his granddaughter with interest as she entered his room and threw herself into a chair.

"Yes. I have."

"And did you see what I wanted you to burn?"

"Burn?" She sat up and looked at him intently. "They're far too interesting to burn! I could only look at one or two things, but——" she stopped. Sir James's face now wore a look of studied detachment. "Grandfather, why, exactly, did you send me down to look at these papers?"

He turned to her and laughed. This alertness pleased him. The Margaret he sought was showing signs of coming back. "I've told you already," he said.

"Did you want to interest me in them for some reason of your own?"

"I said you could find out what you liked from them."

"No. I believe it was more than that."

He did not reply to this.

"I don't want to burn them," she said presently.

"It's just a lot of old stuff."

"Would you think I was being—well—impertinent if I tried to—to trace the story of your love affair with Grandmother?"

"What? Write it down?"

"The idea came to me while I was looking through these things."

"What makes you want to do that?"

"Interest. Why not? You asked me if I didn't feel like writing again. Well, now I want to write your story."

Sir James lay pondering. He had not expected this. He had plotted too well. He did not really want the unearthing of an old story; nor would Charlotte. Yet what did it matter?

He must not risk getting out of sympathy with Margaret if his aim was to help her. "I've always had a feeling to write stories myself," he said with diplomatic irrelevance. "My kind of life gave me plenty of material. I tried once or twice. The knack wasna there. But my fingers have always wanted to put down words. I suppose that's why I wrote my diaries."

"From what I saw this afternoon, Grandfather, I should say you could have written very well."

"No, Maggs. No. But you can try to write our story if you feel like it. You have my permission."

"But you've written books on your work. Miss McQueen said there's a Doctor Somebody helping you with one now. Who is he, by the way?"

"Young Joe Struan? You'll see him working at Woodside Terrace. Aye. He's been helping me. About the brightest student I ever put through my hands. A fine young man, Margaret. A splendid young man."

Now, quite illogically, Margaret decided that she was going to dislike Sir James's paragon very much. She regretted she would have to suffer his presence in what she was already coming to regard as her own domain.

To praise extravagantly in advance is seldom the best way to recommend a friend.

V

It was quite three weeks before she saw him. The beginning of term was a particularly busy time for Doctor Joseph Struan. But what times, indeed, were not particularly busy for the doctor? He was possessed, as Sir James had insisted to Margaret, of much brilliance. But it was a strange brilliance. A brilliance that flourished on overwork, harassment and muddle. There was no use in trying to

[35]

help Struan, to seek to straighten things out for him. At once he would recreate the disorder that seemed necessary to him.

Now he was hurrying along Woodside Terrace, feeling in his pockets for his key to Sir James's rooms. Where was the thing? He must have left it in a pocket when he changed—no. He had worn this suit yesterday, but Miss McQueen would— Oh, good! Here was the key after all! He would just have time to dive down to the basement and see if these papers he had been lent, had got themselves mixed up with— Hello? What was he doing? He had walked past the door! That was the curse of being shortsighted.

He turned back abruptly. In one bound his long legs had cleared the outside steps. Now he had turned the key in the door, banged it behind him and was standing in the twilight of the front hall. How the devil could a man be expected to see if— Oh, here was the switch under his hand.

The sound of diligent typing came from Miss McQueen's room. Should he go in and ask if—? No. He would try to remember to put his head round the door on the way out; then she wouldn't be able to keep him with her talk. Light on the basement staircase? Miss McQueen must have forgotten to— But his legs had carried him down to the bottom before he had thought to the end of the sentence.

He turned the handle of the storeroom door. What? Light here, too? A fire lit? The gleam of someone's hair under the old reading lamp that stood on the table? Hair like— Why hadn't he been told that there was—? But then he had been busy. A faint perfume? Or was he imagining? The same perfume that had hung, vague and pleasant, in the airplane that had brought him north last month. Of course! Why not? Sir James must have sent his granddaughter to— But she had got up, and was coming towards him laughing.

It was so surprising, so ridiculous somehow, merely to turn one's head and be met by the sight of the Frog Footman standing there, enormous and hesitant, in the shadows by the door; peering and blinking at her through his thick, round glasses. "Doctor Struan?"

"Mrs. Raymond?" He stood where he was, paralyzed and shy.

"Yes, we've seen each other before, you know," Margaret said, giving him her hand. "Oh, you won't remember me, but I remember you very well. We flew in the same plane when I was called north several weeks ago. I had no idea the Doctor Struan I have been hearing about would be you!"

[36]

"Oh, well—I suppose I—" The white teeth flashed as he smiled uncertainly.

Taking back the fingers from which the grip of this great, dazed creature had wrung all the blood, Margaret went on: "I do hope I won't be in your way. But there are family papers my grandfather wants me to go through."

"How—how is he?" He had come forward and was standing diffidently beside her at the work table.

Her grandfather's paragon was indeed an odd creature! The square face had turned lobster-red. Margaret felt sorry for him. Could anyone really be so much afflicted by shyness? "Oh, he's much better, thank you."

She saw the thick lenses searching the papers on the table. "I'm sorry. I must try to keep my things more tidy. I laid your papers together and put them over there. Are these—?"

"Oh—oh yes, thank you."

The sheets being tidy, the paragon at once found what he wanted. "Did you mean to work here? Look, I'll—"

"No, no. I'm in a hurry. Thank you." He had felt a frail, disturbing appeal in Margaret Raymond's pale face as she lay back, apparently asleep, in the airplane. Now, as she stood beside him, the light thrown upwards through the faded silk of the old reading lamp gave her face, her eyes, her skin a bright unreality that disturbed him still more. "Well. I think I'll—" He had edged his way to the door again, holding the sheets she had given him.

"Going?"

"Goodbye, Mrs. Raymond." And he was gone, forgetting to shut the door behind him.

She heard his feet mount the stone steps of the basement stairs, and the loud echo in the hall, as the front door crashed shut. Then presently other feet could be heard descending carefully.

"That's the tea."

"Thank you, Miss McQueen. But why should you bother to come down each time?" Margaret spoke from mere politeness. The answer to the question was, she knew: "Curiosity."

"Was that Struan?"

"The paragon? What an extraordinary person!"

"The what?"

"You said my grandfather thought he was a paragon."

[37]

"Well, paragon or no paragon he's dropped half his papers on the stair."

"I expect he'll come back."

"He'll have to." Miss McQueen's expression was smug.

"I'll come in a moment. Then I'll be going home." Margaret turned back to the table and began dumping together a little pile of typewritten sheets.

They contained the first part of the narrative she had set herself to write, and this morning, she had—not without some misgivings—promised to show it to Sir James.

CHAPTER FIVE

I

When the ceremony was over, young James Mennock came out into the sunshine. He felt he must get away from it all. Away from the handshakes and the fuss.

Today he had his special reasons. But at all times he hated formal occasions. And this, his graduation day, his capping day, as it is called in Scotland—and a capping, too, with distinction—was a very formal occasion indeed.

"Of course your father and I must come to see you being capped," his stepmother had said.

At this James had merely looked gloomy.

"Don't you want us, dear?"

"No." And James, heartsore and morose, had begged his father to keep her at home by staying at home himself.

This may have been unkind. But James was glad. For just before the ceremony he had spied his stepmother's relatives waiting for him, ready to pounce, congratulate and invite. He had waved from a distance and eluded them.

And now he had escaped out here in front of the university buildings to be by himself for a time; out and away from those other students—no, not students any more, graduates—who were standing surrounded by adoring mothers, sisters and gratified, black-coated, Edwardian fathers; solemn men who were finding themselves under the pleasant compulsion of having to bestow dignified praise upon these, the very creditable fruit of their own quite admirable loins.

The tall Victorian-Gothic building of Glasgow University stands high and well placed on the brow of Gilmorehill in the west end of the city. And thus, as the ground falls steeply from it, there is little come and go on this, the building's southern frontage.

James came out, still clutching the scroll he had just received. Crossing the front carriageway, he threw himself down on the grass of the slope immediately beyond it. It was hot out here, after the churchlike coolness of the Bute Hall—that part of the building where accomplishment is crowned—and the cellarlike coolness of the cloisters.

The month was July and the day was the 23rd. The less diligent medical students who had failed in their final examinations in December had been allowed this "resit" examination. But with James it was different. With him there had been no lack of diligence. Big-boned, countrified, and strong in appearance, yet he was high-strung, tense and anxious. He had never allowed himself to fail in anything that depended upon his industry. But last December he had been unable to sit, having overstudied, exhausted himself and caught influenza.

For a time he lay there taking cover, a large young man in dark country clothes, his boyish, good-natured face still somewhat pale from overwork, his shock of dark red hair glinting in the sunshine. But presently he sat up, plucked a shoot of grass and thrust the end of it into his mouth. What time was it? He drew out his watch. Time to have lunch, visit his student lodgings, then take himself to St. Enoch's Station and the train to his home in Central Ayrshire. But he had better wait for a moment; wait to give the congratulators and the congratulated time to get their enthusiasms over and be gone. Reflectively he plucked another stem of grass and began to look about him.

II

Down there, appearing from under the arch of a new-built bridge, a Venetian gondola broke the brown waters of the River Kelvin. Now, from a point almost beneath him, there came the sound of rushing wheels and the delighted screams of children and young women as a switchback car plunged giddily on its track. From further away on his left there came a like sound of screaming, then a splash, as the car of the water chute struck the river. For, since the year was 1901, the International Exhibition, the most famous exhibition Glasgow has ever known, lay spread at his feet.

Had James been sitting in the early afternoon of any other July, he would have found himself looking down upon normality; upon a green park with a placid river running through it; a fit and pleasant frame for Glasgow's house of learning. But on this July afternoon, the view from Gilmorehill was filled with towers and gilded domes, white palaces, stucco minarets, and much else that was showy and exotic.

Again the shouts of pleasurable fear came up to him, joined this time by the just distinguishable cry of a turbaned attendant standing outside the Indian theatre and announcing that a performance was about to begin. The exhibition was waking up for the afternoon.

The young man, as he sat there watching on the hillside, sighed because his heart was sore and empty. Yet was that all? Was there not, also, a desire to live? A desire in some way to complete himself. He was, after all, just twenty-three.

But what of the precious scroll lying there on the grass beside him? Was not that a completion? An important milestone? He supposed so. But it had cost him so much; so many early mornings, so many plodding nights. Reluctant hours in wintery lecture rooms. Slum deliveries with their squalor. Cost his hot spirit the endurance of a discipline that could be wearisome, and sometimes insolent, in the wards of city hospitals.

Oh, to be a physician; a healer of the sick was, of course, his calling and his pride! Had a genie risen up in front of him, here, at this moment, told him to choose another profession and offered him a different scroll, he would have refused the genie's offer. But relief may bring reaction. Noses may be held too long to grindstones. Strings, stretched above normal pitch, may jangle as they slacken.

He opened his pocketbook. There it was. The five-pound note that his stepmother had given him as a graduation present. That had indeed been nice of her. It was five pounds' worth of coals of fire. She would no doubt expect him to keep it for such useful things as books or clothing. Still, it was his; his to spend with discretion or to squander.

Why not take it and go down there among the afternoon crowd? Why not try to enjoy himself? What good was he doing, lying here nursing his depression? Why not try to forget?

He scrambled to his feet, drew the chewed grass stems from his mouth, reset his trencher on his dark-red hair, struck the dry grass and seeds from the folds of his graduation gown and went back into the building. He would throw aside these things and go down into the exhibition for an hour or two. If he caught the last train home tonight, what did it matter?

He had been to the exhibition once or twice before, of course. It was impossible, that, working and lodging so near it, he should not.

But the exhibition had, until now, been to him more of an annoyance than a thing of interest. All last winter he had heard the noise of carpenters' hammers as he sat up here in the lecture rooms. And later, when it was opened, fitful bursts of music had come up out of the distance to remind him of a world where people had time to amuse themselves; bursts of music that had challenged earnest purpose and called uncomfortably to his youth.

Ten minutes later he was pushing through the turnstile of what was known as the exhibition's university entrance. He bought himself a guide book and made his way along the main avenue towards the central fountain. Having reached it, he stood looking about him, examining the stucco palaces at closer quarters and deciding what next he had better do.

But now he realized he was hungry. Breakfast had been a long time ago. A half pint of beer and a sandwich or two would, he decided, keep him going. He sat down for a moment on one of the park chairs set in a wide circle round the fountain, opened his guide book and bent over its plan of the grounds. A McKillop's Lager Bar? He would get what he wanted there.

III

But now he was startled by a little scream and looked up. A young girl—of sixteen, perhaps—had stopped in front of him. She had just withdrawn a hand from her bag and it was bleeding profusely.

He jumped up. "Hullo, there?" he called. "What do you think you've been doing?"

Her face as she turned towards him was foolish with distress, although her large, still childish eyes conveyed somehow a look of apologetic laughter. "I've cut my hand."

"So I see. That wasna very sensible. How did you do it?" His voice held some of the tones of rural Ayrshire.

"I cut it on something inside this. I don't know what." She set down her parasol on a chair and trustingly gave him her handbag.

"You've got a scent bottle in here, and it's broken."

"Is that it? I know now. My bag was crushed in the turnstile. It must have broken my lavender water bottle. And just now when I put in my hand for my hankie— Oh, it's frightfully sore! It's nipping like goodness knows what!" She held up the dripping hand ruefully.

[42]

James looked at it professionally. "I can believe you." A smile lit up his face. "If you get scent into a cut it'll nip. Let me see."

She held it out. "Gory sight, isn't it?"

He examined it for a moment. "It's nothing," he said. "It's just a scratch or two. Here," he went on, "come over to the fountain. Wait. I'll take that cartwheel off first. I can't get near to do anything, when you're wearing a thing like that."

She allowed him to take off her wide straw hat and followed him to the fountain. "Will that water be quite pure?" she asked, seeing that he meant to wash the blood from her hand.

"Why shouldn't it? It's running fresh all the time. It's good Loch Katrine water. Have you got your hankie? No. Wait. It'll have scent and glass skelfs in it. I'll take mine." He dipped her hand, then took out the large handkerchief of fine linen that his stepmother, knowing his casualness in these things, had given him for his graduation and, biting an edge, prepared to tear it into strips.

"No! Don't do that! Don't ruin that lovely hankie!"

"Well? What am I to do? Let you bleed to death?"

She laughed at this with the sudden, gay laughter of a young girl. "Is that the only alternative?"

"Yes. The only alternative, as you say."

"Oh, it seems a shame! I say! What great strong teeth you have!"

"Never you heed about my teeth." The handkerchief went into ribbons. "Now we'll get you patched up. Here, sit down." He took a chair from the circle, set it in front of her where she sat and sat down himself. "Look. Hold your hand this way. How do you expect me to bandage it if you hold it like that?"

IV

The girl sat watching his long, deft fingers. Fingers that somehow belied the rest of his loose-boned, country appearance; fingers that seemed to be living a quick life of their own. "What wonderful hands you have!"

"Never you heed about my hands either."

"But I like beautiful hands."

He paid no attention to this.

In a few moments the tying up was done and they found themselves sitting looking at each other, there in the sunshine with the fountain splashing near them. Now he had time to see that the slender child before him had distinction. Who was she? he wondered.

Their eyes met for a moment. And into the face of each there came an uncertain half-smile, a young flush of embarrassment, a sudden turning away.

"You couldn't bear to tie back my hair again, could you? It's all untidy with pulling off my hat. I can't do it properly with one hand."

He could not refuse so direct a request. He pulled out the broad bow of stiff, black silk, caught back her thick, dark hair and retied it deftly.

"I say! How quick you are! You must be used to doing this for your sisters. Are you?"

"No. I've got none."

She turned to look at him, saw that he looked sheepish and turned away again. Then she held out the wounded hand, admiring the neatness of the bandaging. "It's not feeling so sore now," she said. Then as he made no comment, she went on: "What an expert bandage! You must be a doctor! Are you?"

It was on the tip of his tongue to say: "No. But I will be someday." An answer he had given in substance often enough. When suddenly it came to him with a stab of pleasure that "someday" was upon him. That it was here. That it was today.

She wondered why his color had risen again.

"Yes. I *am* a doctor, I suppose," he said.

"Why do you say you suppose? You must either be a doctor or not a doctor. You have to pass examinations, don't you?"

"Yes."

"And be capped?"

"Yes."

"Well then?" She looked at him, puzzled for a moment, then she broke into a delighted laugh. "I know! There was a capping today! You've just newly been turned into a doctor!"

His immediate reply to this was a nod of embarrassment. Then he said: "An M.B. Ch. B. isna a real doctorate."

"Yes, I know all about that. But hadn't I better know your name? I'll have to send you a new hankie anyway."

"Oh, you needna bother about the hankie. My name's James Mennock."

"Doctor James Mennock." She spoke the words slowly, considering their effect. "Haven't you got a middle name?" she asked.

"Yes. It's Bruce. Why?"

"That's better!" she said, still reflecting. "You see, when you're great and famous and are an important surgeon and get a chair at the university and all that sort of thing, you will be able to call yourself Professor Bruce hyphen Mennock. Or—no. Sir James Bruce-Mennock! That would sound all right."

"Lassie, you're blethering!" He was amused, though he did not quite know how to take this nonsense.

"Nothing of the kind! We must all hitch our wagons to stars!"

"You seem to think so, anyway."

"Of course I do! You see, I belong to the university, so I *know* all about these things."

He wondered to whom in the university she belonged; though he was not surprised she should do so, for somehow its stamp was upon her. But he said: "Well, you needna bother about your fancy names for me. I'm going to be a humdrum country doctor. My father's the doctor at Kinaldie. And he's not young. It's time I was helping him down there."

She thought he looked a little rueful as he said this and did not reply at once. Instead she sat looking at the shock of tumbled dark red hair and the long fingers as he took up her bag unbidden and, bending over it, carefully picked out the pieces of broken glass.

"A nice mess you've made of this," he said presently. "You've given it a fine jam in the gates!"

"Yes. But please. Doctor Mennock, don't bother about it. It's not worth much."

He paid no attention to this but went on with what he was doing.

"Listen!" she cried suddenly. "Something has just struck me!"

"Well? What is it now?"

"Is it possible that I have the honor of being the first person to call you *Doctor* Mennock?"

He looked up at her, abashed and smiling, and again nodded slowly.

His companion seemed delighted. "I feel it's tremendously significant, don't you?"

"In what way?" He tried to smile now like a benevolent uncle. But the gap between sixteen and twenty-three was perhaps too narrow for the impersonation quite to succeed.

"Oh, I don't know in what way yet. But just this; you'll see!" She rose and picked up her hat. "Come and help me to find a cup of tea. Think of the terrible loss of blood I've suffered! I must get back my strength. We'll go across to Miss Cranston's teahouse. No. It was burnt the other day, wasn't it? We'll find somewhere else."

He stood up too, giving her back her bag as he did so. But he looked at her uncertainly. In the year 1901 very young ladies did not pick up unknown young men on the grounds of exhibitions. "I'm not sure that I should. Mebbe your folk wouldna like it."

"Don't be ridiculous! You've just saved my life! Besides, I meet all kinds of people by myself here. I'm never out of this place. I've got a season ticket!"

"What kind of people do you meet?"

"Well—school friends, and people like that."

"That's all very well. They're your own kind."

"But aren't you my own kind too?"

He could only laugh at that. This was the spoilt daughter of some grand professor. A girl who was used to indulgence and a way of life that his own simpler background had never given him. "I don't even know who you are," he said guardedly.

"Oh. I'm sorry. I should have told you long ago. My name is Charlotte Gailes."

"The daughter of Professor Mackinnon Gailes?"

"Yes. And now will you come? Or do you want some more of my pedigree?"

So that was who she was? He had never sat at this professor's feet. But of course he knew what he looked like. Mackinnon Gailes, large and shaggily bearded like a prophet of old, storming about its precincts, was a familiar sight to all those of the university.

"Well? What are you waiting for now?" Charlotte asked, adding with mock pompousness, "I've perfect confidence in your good behavior, Doctor Mennock."

Again he laughed. Yet the easily paid compliment pleased him. "I would know better what to do if you would stop talking rubbish," he said. And then, as she did nothing but grin at this, he added: "Well, thanks. I'll come. But when I get home I'll write a letter to your father, just to keep me right."

"Right? And what about keeping *me* right?"

"You too."

"Oh, come along," she said. "You're being ridiculously solemn!"

They went to the Prince's Restaurant as it was near at hand. Now they were sitting in a balcony immediately overlooking the Kelvin River and the switchback railway, with all the sunlit spectacle of the exhibition beyond.

"I only want tea," Charlotte said, her eyes bright with pleasure. "You see, I've just eaten an enormous lunch. Father had invited a lot of fat, foreign professors who are over here to see new inventions or something. They tied their napkins round their necks and went at it, telling us all the time how much better the food was in the countries they came from. But they gobbled everything we put before them all the same."

From this James made a different picture. Mackinnon Gailes' gobbling guests with their napkins round their necks would be men of distinction and knowledge. Of greater knowledge, even, than the professor himself, perhaps. And to James great knowledge was a matter for reverence. He sat thinking of this. But at last, feeling her eyes upon him, he broke silence by saying: "I've had nothing to eat since breakfast."

"Good gracious! Oh, of course! You were being capped. Why didn't you go home first before you came here?"

"I told you I lived in the country."

"Well, never mind. We must get you filled up now as quick as we can." The restaurant was empty and in its early afternoon somnolence. But she jumped up before he could stop her, opened a door and came back with a waitress.

And presently he was swallowing cold beef greedily, yet taking care, a little, of his table manners, lest his companion should want to mock them later, as she had mocked the table manners of the foreign professors.

She sat opposite him watching him, her elbows on the table, her cup of tea held in her two hands. "There now. I'm glad to see you filling up like that. You see, you've got quite a hard afternoon in front of you. You'll need all your strength."

"Strength? Strength for what?"

"All the amusements, of course. We're going on the switchback down there. And then in a gondola, and then down the water chute and round the miniature railway and then into the Indian theatre and everything, and we may even improve our minds a bit by looking at some of the exhibits, although, goodness knows, I've looked at them quite enough! Have you heard the new Edison talking machine in the Grand Avenue?"

"No."

"Oh! I mustn't let you miss that! It's the wonder of—of the century!"

He laughed. "What do you need to go on all these water chutes and things for? I'm sure you've had plenty of all that too."

"I don't *need* to, of course. But you can't have too much of a good thing." And then, with a quick change to earnestness: "But have you come to look at serious things, Doctor Mennock? Things you ought to be seeing, perhaps. I'm being selfish. No. I'll come with you and help you to find whatever you want to see."

"I've been serious for long enough. I'll take you on the water chutes and switchbacks and everything else."

"Now *you're* being unselfish, Doctor."

"No. Honest, Miss Gailes."

"Cross your heart and cut your throat?"

"Aye."

"Well, do it then! Look. Like this."

Looking foolish, he copied her gestures. Her behavior puzzled his matter-of-factness. Was this a young lady's teasing? Or was she nothing but a great schoolgirl, and one who had known nothing but a gentle indulgence? Her confidence in the world was, it seemed, complete. But shouldn't she have more reserve? Be showing the beginnings of poise? In her father's house, surely, she must find opportunity to cultivate these things. "Are you an only child?" he asked.

"Yes. Why? Did you think I was?"

"I wondered."

"But why did you wonder? Is there anything strange about only children?"

"Not that I've heard of." He must not risk appearing too grown-up. He must stay at her level. "What made you think, then?"

"I didna think," James said. "I had heard tell that Professor Mackinnon Gailes had just the one girl. That's all."

"Well, Doctor, I'm that girl!"

There was nothing to do but be amused at this and go on munching, his eyes on his plate. When he raised them again he found Charlotte looking at him intently.

"I've just been wondering," she said.

"Well, what is it this time?"

"No. At home they call me an inquisitive monkey! But I can't help being interested, can I?"

"Go on." He laid down his fork and knife and looked at her.

"Well, you have a father, haven't you? And a mother?"

"A stepmother, anyway."

"Oh!" Charlotte's only ideas about stepmothers were gleaned from the fairy tales of her nursery days. They had left her prejudiced. Her face reflected what she was thinking.

James took up his fork and knife again and went on eating. "Oh, she's not as bad as that!" he said.

She colored hotly. "I didn't mean—"

"What were you going to ask me, anyway?"

"I was only thinking it was queer neither of them came to such an important thing as your capping."

"I wouldn't let them."

"Wouldn't—?" Perhaps she should ask no more. But curiosity won. "But Doctor Mennock, whyever not?"

"I dinna want any fuss."

"Oh? Why?"

But his eyes were on his plate again. He was eating solemnly and diligently and did not answer. When, in a little while, he raised them, Charlotte's expression was all self-reproach.

"Oh, Doctor Mennock, I'm sorry! Mother's always lecturing me about this inquisitiveness!"

"What are you sorry about?"

"I've said something to annoy you!"

"No. A friend of mine that should have been there wasna there. If he—" James shrugged and looked about him vacantly.

She watched him, bewildered for a moment. But now a quick guess had given her the answer. "Don't tell me any more, Doctor." Her inexperience was retreating before pain. Or was she being selfish? "Unless you want to."

He turned to her again. Her eyes were big with distress and that sense of being at a loss, of not knowing enough to be able to respond with the right show of feeling, which comes to the young and the sensitive.

"We both had the influenza in the winter," James said. "I got better. He didna."

"Was he a great friend?"

James nodded. And then to reassure her: "Oh, don't you bother your head about me. I'm fine."

But now, for the moment, she had forgotten everything but sympathy. "No. Tell me about him. Did you go through the university together?"

Again he nodded. "And we should have been capped together today."

"I see now why you didn't want any fuss."

"Do you?" Why did her words please him so much?

"Yes. Of course! Anybody would!"

"No. Not anybody." His stepmother, for instance. For her an occasion was an occasion. No matter what the overtones. But at once this young girl with her quick feelings, her promise of delicate womanliness, had seen it. And now, as a result, his tongue was loosed and he found himself telling her of his friend.

VI

It was a David and Jonathan story. Young Lermont and he, both of them shy and knowing little of the town, had come up at the same time from their different villages to the university. A chance meeting on the first day of their first term had drawn like to like. Hard-working and serious, on the defensive, yet with the arrogance that comes with brilliance, they had stuck together, founded a closed community of two, taking little heed of others or of the life around them. After two years Lermont had lost his father and his mother had come to Glasgow. For a time James had joined them to make a household of three. There he had been happy and quite as much at home as in Kinaldie. And then last winter Lermont had gone, taking his great promise with him.

"I got a letter from Mrs. Lermont yesterday," James concluded. "Just to wish me luck for today." He had, of course, merely given Charlotte outlines. But now, as he sat back watching her large eyes swimming, he asked himself with surprise why he should have told this child these things. What strange quality did she possess that he had felt he must?

"How good of her to send it!" Charlotte said fervently.

"I'm going to see Mrs. Lermont later today," he said.

"Oh I'm glad, Doctor!" But now, with these confidences, Charlotte's youth could not help feeling flattered and important. Looking at James as he sat back, having finished his roast beef, she decided that he must indeed be a very sad and wonderful man. She groped in her bag for her handkerchief, then remembering that there might still be chips of glass in it, she took up a table napkin and furtively wiped her eyes with a corner of it. James Mennock, though he did not know it, was in great danger of turning into a hero.

He stood up. "Come on then. We'll get a start made on the switchback. It's the nearest."

His words came as a shock, dropping her down to earth. "But Doctor Mennock, are you sure you want to?"

"Of course. Didn't I tell you I wanted to?"

She stood waiting while he paid what they owed. Was this bravery for her sake? Or could older people put trouble away from them so easily as that? Or was life just a checkerboard where white followed black?

They had done all the amusements, heard the wonders of the talking machine, sat for a time listening to a military band and had finally drunk chocolate together at the Van Houten Pavilion. Now, two hours later, they were standing again at the university entrance. He held out his hand.

"But Doctor Mennock, I must pay you!"

He was dumbfounded. "Pay?"

"Yes. For all you've been spending on me."

"No, Miss Gailes, you owe me nothing. It's been a pleasure. Honest, it has!"

"But it wouldn't be fair not to let me pay my share!"

"You're not doing it, anyway."

"Well, you told me you lived in Kinaldie in Ayrshire. I'll send it there. And a new hankie too."

"I'll send back your money."

"Oh dear! I'll have to talk to my parents about this. Goodbye, then. I do hope we shall see each other again soon. I should hate to lose sight of you!"

He stood, watching and wondering about her, as she went off up University Avenue, a slender young girl in a white dress and a large straw hat, swinging her closed parasol in the hand that was unbandaged.

When she was out of his sight, he turned away. Now he must pay his respects to the mother of his dead friend.

CHAPTER SIX

I

"May I come in, Henry? Or are you working?"

"Come in, my dear. Come in."

Charlotte's mother advanced into the professor's study; a room of bookshelves and leather-upholstered dignity in the house they occupied within the university precincts. She was sorry to find him sitting in his armchair looking unapproachably cheerful. Unapproachably because experience at once told her that it would be difficult, in his present mood, to bring him down to the level of a serious conversation.

Edith Mackinnon Gailes' portrait had been painted by a young American artist named Sargent. Her father, a shipping magnate of Glasgow, had commissioned the portrait at the time of her marriage as a present to his son-in-law, the professor. It was a masterpiece, capturing and emphasizing the almost too thin elegance, the almost too confident good breeding, of a woman just approaching thirty-five. To Edith, her picture had become an obsession and a key. Unnoticed by others and now from habit unnoticed almost by herself, she was forever consulting her reflection in mirrors to see if she had grown fatter or thinner, more lined or more rounded, than the handsome woman hanging in the drawing room upstairs.

Mechanically she did so now, casting a searching look into the mirror, large, gilded and Victorian, that crowned the study mantelpiece; reassured herself for an instant that seventeen years had not been at all unkind to her, then looked down at her husband.

The professor sat, lion-maned and Jovelike, reading a paper of some kind, slapping the thick leather arm of his chair with delight and emitting chuckles as he read. He looked over his spectacles at his wife.

"I say, Edie, this is great fun! That Heidelberg man who was here with the others at lunch left this lecture of his for me. He thinks he knows everything there is to know! But listen to this." The professor read aloud a long and involved sentence in the German tongue, then looked up happily. "Smug, isn't it?"

Edith replied to this with a smile that was placating and perfunctory. "Yes. Very," she said falsely. She had indeed, like many of her kind and generation, been to school in Germany. But her grasp of German had never been anything more than sketchy; and thirty odd years is ample time for a grasp to relax. Besides, had her husband read the sentence to her in the clearest of English, she would still not have understood its technicalities. The professor, she reminded herself, was like that. He kept forgetting that his own very special knowledge was not the common knowledge of all mankind. But now she must really be firm with him.

"Henry," she began severely, "put that down. I want to talk to you. I must know what you think we ought to do."

He laid the paper on his knees with reluctance, put his spectacles aside, joined his fingertips together and sat looking at her. "Do you, my dear? But you always know what to do. Why are you coming to me?"

"No, Henry, this is a little serious. It's about Charlotte."

"Charlotte?" His attention was caught by his daughter's name, as Edith had intended it should be. "Well?"

She reversed the swivel chair before his work desk, sat down and turned towards him. "Charlotte went out after lunch. She said she was going for a walk in the exhibition grounds. You've probably never bothered to notice what she does, but she's been going quite often on these fine afternoons. I've never seen any reason why she shouldn't. She often meets girls she knows. It's not as though it were late in the evening or anything."

"Yes, but—"

"Well, a little while ago she came back and blithely told me that she had been spending the whole afternoon with a young man."

"But, Edie, we know lots of young men, and—"

"This was one we don't know."

"And was he a nice young man?"

"Henry! He was a stranger! And how can a child so foolishly innocent as Charlotte know if a strange young man is nice or nasty?"

"I've always considered that Charlotte had an excellent instinct, my dear."

"That's all very well. Please remember that the child is only sixteen!"

"I'm a great believer in instinct, you know."

"Henry, will you be serious! Just for once."

He saw now that she was distressed. Saw too that she had perhaps some reason for being so. He got up, stretched his great frame, stroked his hair and beard, then turning his back to the empty fireplace, stood looking down upon his wife from under heavy eyebrows. "Tell me more about this, Edie."

"Well, as I say, Charlotte came in just now. Her hand was bound up in a torn handkerchief. She had cut it on a broken scent bottle or something—oh, nothing at all—and this young man had bound it up for her."

Here Mrs. Gailes stopped, listened for a moment, then lowered her voice as she heard a sound outside. "There she is, I think," she said.

"Have you lectured her about this?" he asked quietly.

"No. I wanted your advice first."

II

Charlotte was the single and much-prized fruit of a marriage that had been contracted when neither of her parents could any longer be called young. And thus, as a consequence, it was seldom indeed that the winds of heaven were allowed to visit her roughly.

They watched her now as she crossed the somber room and flung herself down in the great armchair her father had just stood up from.

"Well, young lady?" he said, looking at her bandaged hand. "Been in the wars?"

"Cut it on my lavender water bottle at the exhibition. Hasn't Mother told you?"

"Who bound it up for you?"

"It's beautifully done, don't you think?" She sat up in the chair holding up her hand admiringly. "It was a young man called Doctor James Bruce Mennock. He tore up his beautiful linen handkerchief to do it. We must buy one like it and send it to him."

"We must, indeed, if he has been destroying his handkerchief on your account. Yes. It's very neatly tied. And where does Doctor Mennock practice? Or perhaps he didn't tell you that?"

"He was only capped today. Oh, yes, he told me all about himself. But I've been telling Mother all this."

Mrs. Gailes made no comment.

"I liked him," Charlotte went on. "After he had done my hand, I discovered he hadn't had any lunch, so we went to the Prince's Restaurant."

"With a strange young man, my dear?"

"Oh, doctors are always respectable. *He* certainly was. He was a nice creature!"

The professor put back his large head and gave a loud laugh. "Describe this nice creature to me, my dear," he said, thus earning a questioning look from his wife.

Henry could get into dreadful muddles, practical and social, Edith reminded herself. But now and then he could be good with Charlotte. Better indeed than she, her mother could be. His love for his daughter seemed at times to lend him tact and wisdom that were quite untypical of him. She had better leave the child to him and see what he could do.

"Oh, I don't know," Charlotte answered. "Downright country voice. He came from Kinaldie in Ayrshire. His father's the doctor there. Shaggy and solemn. Dark-red hair that wouldn't lie down much. Rather like a sheepdog, I should say. Eyes that had an amused glint in them somewhere."

"I'm not sure about that glint, Charlotte."

"But it was a lovely glint, Father!"

"I see."

Now, as so often happened with her husband, Edith Gailes could not decide where seriousness stopped and irresponsibility began. But she still said nothing.

"Oh, and I forgot to tell you—I don't think I told *you* either, Mother —he had the most amazing hands! Well, you see what he did with this bandage, don't you?" She stopped here, then added inconsequently: "I wish *I* had long fingers." She threw herself back into the deep chair and held up her unbound hand, examining it childishly.

"He may turn into a great surgeon." There was irony in his tone.

"That's what I told him, Father." But now sensing disapproval, Charlotte stopped here and looked at each of her parents in turn. It was almost in a tone of pleading that her next words were spoken. "Doctor Mennock was terribly sad and unhappy. His greatest friend would have been capped with him today. But he died of influenza last winter."

"Doctor Mennock seems to have told you quite a number of things, my dear."

"Well, of course! We spent the afternoon together!"

"Together? Doing what?"

"Water chutes, switchbacks, and this and that. I thought he mightn't want to. But he was very brave about his sorrow, and I think it cheered him up. Oh, and by the way, we must send him the money for those things when we send his handkerchief. We must insist! He paid for everything this afternoon."

Here Charlotte's mother was glad to see the professor put his hands behind his back and look thoughtfully at the floor. "Yes," he said. "We must send the money to him." And then in a moment, and with something of an effort: "Charlotte, I don't quite like this. Your mother had told me of it before you came in just now. Oh, I know it was all as innocent as the day on your part, but it rather stamps the young man, I think, that he—he lent himself to this—this escapade."

"But I insisted! It was I who asked him to come with me!"

Her father considered this. "Well, that makes him a little better and you a little worse," he said at length. "But I'm quite ready to believe it's not a very bad worse. And of course you were grateful to him for patching you up. Oh, I daresay Doctor Mennock is quite a good sort of young man. Your instinct would have told you if he hadn't been, I think. Still, even if you were foolish enough to ask him to come with you, he was grown-up, and should have known to refuse; for your sake, if not for his own." Pausing in his harangue, Henry Gailes sought the eyes looking up at him, surprised now and large with tears. "No, Charlotte," he went on. "This just must not happen again. I know your mother thinks I encourage you to be irresponsible sometimes. Well, perhaps I do. This—this casual afternoon with a young man in the exhibition is partly my fault, I daresay. But we'll both tell her now that we're sorry, shall we? And that we're growing up and finding our dignity. And your mother will buy Doctor Mennock a new handkerchief and we'll send it to him with the money he spent on you, and after that we'll forget all about this."

As he concluded, he bent down to kiss his daughter's brow. The act brought her to her feet and released the flood.

"Charlotte, Charlotte!" He stood behind her, caught her slight, trembling shoulders and turned her towards her mother. "There," he said. "We're sorry for what we've both done. We're going to stick to people that we know after this. Now, my dear, run upstairs and wash your face!"

The professor collapsed exhausted into his chair when their daughter had left them. "Well?" he asked ruefully. "Did I say the right things to the poor child?"

His wife patted the high knob of hair on the top of her head, ran a nervous finger round the inside of her high Edwardian neckband and allowed a pale smile to brighten her face. "Yes, Henry. I think you did. You were very lenient, of course."

"What else could I be?"

She shrugged.

"You know, Edie," he went on presently, "I should imagine that the Tree of the Knowledge of Good and Evil hasn't done much more than cast its shadow on Charlotte so far."

"I wonder if it has done much more than that to you."

"I know you think I'm just an old silly."

She got up from the swiveled chair, straightened her tall body, put her hands on her slim hips and looked down upon him in her turn. "Quite a nice silly, sometimes," she said. "Still, he might have been any sort of—of loiterer. What kind of young man would you guess he was?"

"A country lad with no harm in him, I should say. Someone who has no real idea about things. We have lots of students like that, of course."

"His father is a country doctor, it seems."

"Country doctors can be very simple people, Edie. I could find out about him easily enough."

"I shouldn't trouble. But we must write to him saying how surprised we are to hear what has happened, that you enclose whatever amount you decide on, and that you now consider the matter finished with."

"Oh, dear me, yes! I shall have to write him a letter, I suppose!"

"Of course!"

"You'll have to help me with it, Edie."

"I knew you would say that."

"Oh, let us leave it this evening. We must think exactly how to put it. We'll sleep on it and write tomorrow."

III

The professor, his wife noted, took his own advice and slept as well as usual. Judging from the sounds coming through the open door of his dressing room, Charlotte's folly had not disturbed his rest. But that was Henry. Too slow to catch alarm and too ready to believe it over. Still, she felt she had been right in sitting silent, leaving him to admonish their daughter. For some strange reason he could touch the quick of Charlotte's feelings with a touch that she, her mother, did not possess. Awake and worried though she was, Edith's good sense decided she had better say nothing more to Charlotte. Why underline further an incident that had after all been quite harmless, by giving it an importance, implying a seriousness it had much better not have?

Yet she could not but feel disquieted about it. At sixteen Charlotte was too old to be so ridiculously innocent, so foolishly trusting, so cheerfully indiscreet as to allow herself to fall into a casual but obviously enthusiastic friendship with a strange young man; allow herself to be "picked up," as was the vulgar term for such conduct, Edith understood.

And there was that letter to be written by her husband. Charlotte could not possibly be allowed to take entertainment from this so-called doctor, about whom they knew nothing. Besides, whoever he was, he must not be left to boast that he had casually—yes—"picked up" Professor Mackinnon Gailes' daughter and rioted round the exhibition with her, without anything being said. What kind of name would this give her? What kind of people did he think they were?

Henry had promised to write the letter but of course he would not have the faintest idea what to say. In the morning, she would have to stand at his shoulder dictating it. The letter must be worded strongly; with dignity, of course, but without venom. At the same time the chill wind of their disapproval must blow through it. This forward creature must be shown that, having performed the slight service of bandaging Charlotte's hand, he had not thus established any sort of right to friendship with her. But just what to say? How word it?

Ideas and sentences chased each other round Edith's head as she lay watching the shadows cast upon her bedroom wall by a lamp shining through the leaves of a tree just outside her window; shadows that danced as the summer night wind stirred the leaves. And there was Henry in his dressing room, sleeping the sleep of a boy, as though exhibition parks, doubtful young men and foolish girls had never been heard of!

But James Mennock had forestalled her.

His letter lay on the top of the next morning's breakfast pile. For a long moment, after opening it, the professor gazed at the signature. "Mennock? Now who is James B. Mennock? Oh!" A half-smile lit his face. "Charlotte's friend!"

Edith watched him as he read, then reread it. His expression did not alter though he took what seemed to her a maddening amount of time. But at last he looked at her over the top of his spectacles.

"Well, my dear," he said, "this poor boy doesn't seem exactly a criminal."

"How do I know what he seems, until I read what he has written? Quickly, Henry, before Charlotte gets down!"

He threw it across to her and took up his other letters.

Glasgow
23rd July, 1901.

DEAR PROFESSOR MACKINNON GAILES,

I am putting this into the post before I leave Glasgow tonight, as I feel it is my duty to write to you at once. Miss Gailes will have told you that she spent the afternoon with me at the exhibition. It happened because I bandaged her hand which she had cut slightly. After I had done this, she invited me to come for a cup of tea and then go round with her. As I saw that she was grateful for the small service I had done her, I consented. But first I told her I would write this letter to you.

Let me assure you, sir, that no harm came to Miss Gailes while she was in my company. I was at all times fully aware that she was a very genteel and well brought up young lady and she was treated accordingly.

She spoke of asking you to repay me the small amount I spent on her amusement. You would only insult me if you tried to do so.

I remain, sir, yours respectfully,

JAMES B. MENNOCK

"Am I to have no breakfast this morning, my dear?"

"I'm sorry, Henry." She put down James's letter and set about her duties.

"Well? Doesn't know what's what, perhaps? But not a criminal, would you say? And he's one up on us by getting in first."

"Oh, it's not a question of criminals, Henry! And I don't see what difference this letter makes. If not knowing what's what, as you put it, means he doesn't know his proper place, then I certainly agree with you. He'll have to be written to this morning just as we planned. Whatever he is, he's going to be paid his money back. What right has a ridiculous young man like that to force us to be obliged to him, whether we want to or not?"

"Let's have another look at it." He now held it up to the light, reading it critically with his bushy eyebrows as well as his eyes. "No. Not a nasty letter, I should say, Edie. Simple, even foolish. But no, not the letter of a nasty young man."

"There's your coffee, Henry," she said, "and don't spill it."

CHAPTER SEVEN

I

It was late afternoon. Sir James Mennock sat alone in his down-stairs library staring at the moving flames of his fire. This room had also become his bedroom. He could get about with a stick now and he wanted to be near his books. On his knee were the first two chapters of his granddaughter's narrative. Only a few minutes ago he had finished reading them aloud to his wife.

For a time he remained thinking about these and about their writer. Strange girl, Margaret. Strange, that she should want to go searching back down the years like this. Strange that this desire had been so strong in her that he had been able to use it as a bond to hold her here at home. But he felt he had been justified. As a result, Margaret seemed less brittle. And her laughter had become gayer. Her elegance less frail.

And these chapters? The child had done very well with them, really. The exhibition of 1901 was, of course, easy. There was material in the libraries. And her story was interesting. But was it his story? Or Charlotte's? He could not think so. She had invented too much, surely? Or was his own memory playing him tricks? His sitting out there on the grass after the capping, for instance. That was invented. It was most unlikely he should hide himself away like that. If he had wanted to avoid lunching with his relatives, wouldn't he simply have told them he had something else to do?

But here at hand on his side table was his diary for the year 1901. He had told Margaret to bring it home. He turned to July 23rd.

So I went down to the front bank and hid from Connie's sister and her husband. I couldn't be bothered being polite to them. I was in a queer frame of mind anyway. I sat on the bank chewing grass and wondering why the devil I had ever been born. Reaction, very likely. Decided to shake off the blues by going to the exhibition before I went to see John Lermont's mother.

[61]

Sir James smiled to himself. He had forgotten all about this! No. He could not fault Margaret there. But the ribbon-tying incident? Had that ever happened?

Then, when I had got her hand bandaged, she asked me to tie back her hair for her. If I had thought the girl was trying to be too clever I wouldn't have done it. But I saw it wasn't to make me admire her hair or anything. She just wanted it tied. That was all. So I did it.

And she talked all the time. But it was mostly blethers. The comic talk of an only bairn, that has had too much petting and attention. I would say she was very young for her age.

And their talk in the restaurant?

I don't know why I should have spoken about John Lermont's death. And why telling her seemed to help. There were tears in her eyes.

Miss Gailes looks to me like turning into a fine sympathetic woman in a year or two. She should make a good wife to some man.

Again Sir James smiled to himself. This time at his own record of his young pompousness. He had not looked at these pages for very many years. Almost all that was left to him of his graduation day was the picture of a young girl in a white dress walking with him in the sunshine. He sat thinking of this. Yes. Time must play tricks with memory.

In a long attachment, he supposed, at first passionate, then warmly affectionate and increasingly interdependent, each succeeding stage must dim, must falsify, the picture, the climate, of earlier, younger years. Until these became mere dwindling memories of memories, ever becoming less distinct behind the mists of later feeling. Mists only to be pierced by sudden, poignant things. Birdcalls. A taste in the mouth. A phrase of music. Indeed, taste and hearing, now he came to think of it, were memory's closest friends. Even the sight of old photographs, of faded letters, could seldom do so much to bring things back.

Was it possible that his granddaughter was now better in tune with the young James Mennock than he, the old James Mennock could be? Had she caught the right echoes from his own pages? Had she come nearer to these two who had been the very young Charlotte and himself, using her own youth to read theirs?

For a time Sir James continued to hang over his diary, checking Margaret at random. Then, on hearing the outside door bang, he set sheets and diary to one side and sat back.

No. He must change his verdict. The girl's narrative had, it seemed to him, come very close.

II

His granddaughter entered the room looking apprehensive. She was followed by Lady Mennock.

"I've crept back!" Margaret said.

"Very good, Maggs. Not bad at all. Your grandmother and I think you've done very well. Don't we, Charlotte?" Sir James looked slyly at his wife.

"Of course I think it's very clever of Margaret, indeed. I can't imagine how she got to know so much about us. But—"

There was a spark in the old man's eye as he set the tips of his long fingers together. "What does that 'but' mean?"

"Well, for one thing, I don't think she has been quite fair to my parents."

"But Granny! You've been telling me all about them yourself! Haven't I been plaguing you with questions? Now take my great-grandfather first. Where have I gone wrong with him? I'm not being positive, darling, I only want to know."

There were no diaries on her grandmother's side. But Margaret had considered the old professor easy. Lady Mennock had told her much of course and Sir James had added to the picture of his wife's father.

"Mackinnon Gailes? A nice kinna big man, Maggs. A fine scholar. A real professor. Looked like King Lear. Thoughts in the clouds. Old clothes. No business sense. Managed by his wife. Your Granny liked him better than she liked her mother, although she will never say she did. And he could manage her better than his wife could."

But it was old Polly, Lady Mennock's parlormaid, who had brought him most vividly to life for Margaret. "A fine old man, Miss Margaret. An' verra weel learnt, I hear. A grand gentleman! Verra soft-hearted. The kinna man that would gang roon' the hoose lettin' the mice oot o' the traps. Aye. An' lookin' like the prophet Abraham a' the time

[63]

he was doin' it! Oh, an' he'd his fun aboot him as weel. Ye would whiles see him teasin' her Ladyship!"

"By her Ladyship, do you mean Lady Mennock's mother, Polly?" There had been no reproof in this. Margaret had merely asked for information. But at once the temperature had dropped.

"Aye. That's the one I mean, Miss Margaret." And Polly had withdrawn coldly and with a flounce.

Lady Mennock had been thinking. "It's difficult to say just what you've done, Margaret. No. I think you've made my father seem a little silly."

"Silly?"

"Your great-grandfather could be—I don't know—far away, perhaps. But not silly."

"But I don't think I *have* made him silly, darling. Quite the reverse. Wasn't it he who took you in hand and lectured you?"

But Sir James, now Margaret's warm partisan, had become impatient. "Oh, it's no use talking to your Granny, Maggs! It's an excellent description of your father, Charlotte. Excellent! Couldn't be better."

His wife turned upon him angrily. "James! Perhaps you'll allow me to know my own father better than you ever did!"

Though he loathed being contradicted, Sir James did not reply to this. He merely sat glumly looking before him.

Margaret hastened to close the rift with another question. "And what about my great-grandmother Mackinnon Gailes, Granny?"

"Your great-grandmother wrote and read German very well, Margaret. Much better than my father ever did. She used to help him in his work."

"I am sorry. I had guessed she would be like most other Victorian girls, and would look on schooling abroad merely as a decoration."

"Well, you were quite wrong."

"Any way, that's easily put right. What else?"

Lady Mennock sat thinking for a time. "You've made my mother too—I don't know—too unyielding, too formal. Not as I remember her."

Margaret had found Edith Gailes more difficult. The Sargent portrait had told her of her great-grandmother's handsomeness, her conscious poise and that look of arrogance, which may have had its roots in shyness. Or so Lady Mennock believed at all events. Her mother, she had told Margaret, was a very shy person. Sir James, who had never really liked her, declared she was self-assured and none too sensitive. But Margaret, hotly determined to see from everybody's angle, had not accepted this. Perhaps great-grandmother Mackinnon Gailes was a blind spot in her grandfather's otherwise excellent understanding. "I didn't think I had made her very unyielding and formal, Granny."

But Lady Mennock, engaged in examining her memories, did not reply to this quite directly. "No. Beneath her shyness my mother was warm and vulnerable. I loved my mother, Margaret."

"But, darling! Of course!"

"And I didn't like that bit about her comparing herself to her portrait. No. I wouldn't say my mother had any vanity."

Sir James exploded. "Rubbish, Charlotte! Of course your mother had vanity! Lots of it! She was a good-looking woman! Don't you tell me your mother didna hold Mrs. Mackinnon Gailes in the very highest esteem! What way should she not compare herself to her portrait?"

"Well, really, James! So I'm not to be allowed to know my own mother either? That's just too much!"

The old man sat back in his chair nursing his annoyance. "Oh, I knew your mother fine!" he muttered gloomily. "You've got nothing at all to tell me about your mother!"

Again Margaret hastened to pour oil. "Darlings! No! Not this kind of behavior to each other, please! Look. If writing down these things is going to upset you, then I promise you I won't write another word!"

Her grandmother looked at her with surprise. "But Margaret, it's most interesting! We don't want you to stop! Do we, James?"

"But if you say there's no truth in it?"

"Who said there was no truth in it?" Lady Mennock rose from her chair and went towards the door. "Oh, little bits here and there, like what I've been telling you. But it's so lovely being reminded of all these things! And we can always keep you right, you know. Aren't you changing into something else for dinner?"

When his wife was gone, Sir James began to unwind from about him the resentful gloom in which he was now wrapped. His eyes, slowly rising to look up into his granddaughter's, caught fire from the spark of laughter they found there. But he did not allow himself to smile. He merely shook his head in mock resignation. "There you are, Maggs!" he said. "That's your grandmother for you! She was always

[65]

like that. A changeable, flighty body! Now you see what I've had to put up with for more than fifty years!"

III

"Doctor Struan will never get here today, Mrs. Raymond."

It was the next morning, and frostily bleak, with the bleakness of early December.

Margaret stood pulling off fur gloves in Miss McQueen's sanctum. By now she was used to these dreary greetings. "But why not, Miss McQueen?"

"Fog."

"But there was scarcely any when I came in just now."

"No. But there will be. They say it's dense on the south side of the river. That's where Struan comes from."

"I promised to work with him this morning. I expect he'll come if he can."

"Oh, he'll come if he can! He's always coming here if he can—now."

Since Miss McQueen had spoken the last sentence in a breathy whisper, and mostly to herself, Margaret chose to ignore it. The implication that her own coming to Woodside Terrace was of any interest to the paragon, other than that he had found she was able to type rapidly to his dictation and thus help with her grandfather's work, was of course absurd.

Miss McQueen's thoughts were still with the weather. "I hate fog," she said.

"Does it affect you?"

"Asthma."

"I'm so sorry."

"I had a terrible time two years ago. I couldn't lie down. Sat up in bed for a whole fortnight! Gasping for my life!"

"How dreadful!"

"Six pillows! No. Seven! Would you like this cup of tea?"

"Thank you." Margaret did not want the tea Miss McQueen was pouring out for her but she felt she must accept it as a gesture of sympathy. "I'll take it downstairs with me. And look at some of my own things, while I wait to see if he's going to appear or not."

Her basement had become a strangely engrossing place. The fascination of her self-imposed task had taken hold of her. The effort drew upon her forces, stimulating and exciting them. Here, in these last weeks, she had lived hours of discovering, condensing and writing; too much obsessed to note that once again she was indeed touching the fringes of contentment.

And now the results had received the approval of her grandparents. Or at least of Sir James. This morning the old man had called her to him. "Go on with this, Maggs," he had said. "You know more about the way the world wags than I gave you credit for."

"How you and Granny wagged, you mean?"

"Oh, everybody wags in much the same way. But go on. I want to see how you'll work it out."

Margaret stood for a time looking into the fire that was now lit each morning against her coming. Its springing flames warmed her transparent skin and caught copper lights in her hair. Then perhaps after all she had not been chasing shadows? Donald had always said she could write. The making of this record might lead her into the developing of a gift.

And in the meantime—Chapter III. Kinaldie. Her grandfather's young background. But this morning was promised to the paragon. She turned to look up through the bars of her basement window. Was the fog becoming thicker? Tiresome if he were held up. She would look as she had said, at something else while she hung on, waiting.

She crossed to the rack and unlocked a tin box containing papers from the 'twenties. These too had been carefully docketed by Sir James. Letters written to her father by her grandparents. Letters written by him to them. She picked up a bunch penned in her father's hand. From one of these the corner of a photograph protruded. She brought the bundle over to the table and untied the tape.

The photograph, together with a letter, had been thrust back into an envelope which was addressed to her grandfather and bore an Austrian stamp. Margaret sat down at the table and held the picture under the work lamp.

IV

It was a snapshot of her father when he was twenty—she learned the year from the dating of his letter—standing in a bathing slip on a divingboard over some Tyrolese lake, threatening, as it seemed, to drench the photographer with a pail of water. A beautiful, laughing

[67]

boy, his dark hair wet on his brow, his legs apart, his young body poised in the act of throwing. And behind him pine trees and towering snow mountains.

A quick emotion took Margaret unawares as she bent over the little picture. A tear gathered and fell; she did not know why.

The letter was addressed from the Salzkammergut in Austria and was dated August 4, 1924.

My dear wonderful Father!

I write at once as you told me to do. But how really tremendous of you! I got the letter yesterday and at once went to collect the money in Ischl. It had arrived, so all is well.

And *please*, *please* don't worry about me any more! Everything is absolutely above board and straightened out now. Yes, I've told you everything. I swear it! I immediately repaid Jim the money I had borrowed. And now I hereby do as you ask me, and solemnly promise yourself and the old lady always to come to you in future, if I am stuck, and not to borrow from friends. Least of all from those you don't know. From now on you can have complete faith in my word. Please do believe that! I love you both much too dearly to have you troubling about me!

I shall now stay here at Hallstatt for about two weeks longer, I think. I simply must! Please don't be annoyed about this. I find I can manage it beautifully after repaying Jim. The others are staying until the end of the month, but I promise I shall tear myself away in a fortnight's time.

This is the most lovely place I have ever seen. It hurts to think of ever leaving it. I must bring you both here some time. It would kill you! I enclose a snap Jim took. You can see the mountains behind me and how wonderful they are, and the pinewoods and the lake and everything.

All the love I possess to the dearest, most forgiving parents in the world, and again a million thanks!

Your unsatisfactory but repentant

Sandy

Margaret sat considering this, guessing at the story that lay behind it. The end of a rumpus over money with her grandfather weakly giving in and sending more? Had her grandparents spoilt their only son hopelessly? Were they too anxious to see him happy?

Again she took up the photograph. No. She could hardly blame them for wanting to give the moon to this handsome, laughing boy.

And yet it was an odd letter; a letter suggesting a slipperiness somewhere; suggesting, even, that its writer did not always stick to the truth. She knew little about very young men. But it seemed to her that, for a Mennock at least, these expressions of affection were too effusive; that they came too easily, too glibly to the end of his pen. Had her father become expert in gauging just how much his doting parents would swallow? And did he quite deliberately use this doubtful accomplishment? Or was she being unjust? It would have pleased his daughter, now, to be told that she was.

Ought she to show this photograph to the old people? They had dozens, of course. At every stage of her father's life. Photographs so familiar to herself that they told her nothing. But this new snap had caught so poignantly, so vividly, his charm, his young inconsequence, that Margaret could not look at it unmoved. Would the sight of it merely remind them of some old unhappiness? Bring them more pain than pleasure?

She thought of the words in her grandfather's diary written on the day of her birth. "Alexander being Alexander." What sort of young man had her father been? And what had he cost his parents in worry and heartbreak?

V

The paragon found her sitting brooding over the photograph. He tiptoed about, genteel and apologetic, taking off his overcoat, excusing his lateness, talking about the fog. At length, ready to begin, he came close and stood over her, peering shyly down through his strong spectacles. He did not mind that she continued quite still, bending over the little photograph in her hand. He was glad to go on merely standing there beside her. But why was she so *very* still? "Are you all right, Mrs. Raymond?"

She did not answer him at once. Then, in another moment, she turned to look up and say: "I've just found this. It's a snapshot of my father."

The paragon took it from her, wondering if he were imagining tones of emotion in her voice. He stood blinking at the picture; examining Alexander Mennock's young handsomeness; made conscious of what had been denied to himself. But what did she expect him to say? "Yes," he said at length, "I've—I've heard that Sir James's son had very good looks."

"Do you think that's any help to a man, Doctor?"

"Yes. If he has character."

"I'm beginning to wonder if my father had."

How was he to answer that? What had they told her?

But now Mrs. Raymond swung round in her chair the more easily to look up at him. "Did you ever hear that my father was—well, spoilt and unreliable?"

The paragon turned the color of a lobster. "I've heard things said at the university, Mrs. Raymond."

"Do you know, Doctor Struan, this is the first time I ever heard that my father *went* to the university?"

He looked foolish and began to fumble among his papers. "Oh, I shouldn't—maybe, they wouldn't—"

"Wouldn't what, Doctor? Wasn't my father a success at the university? Was he sent down or something?"

He started. He did not want to reply to this. If her grandparents had not told her about their son, why must he?

But her eyes were upon him. "Doctor, tell me. It will kill me until I know."

"Sir James—Professor Mennock as he was then—was warned in time and got him away."

"But what had he done?"

It was a relief to the other that he could tell her in all honesty that he did not know; that he could only sit down now and begin arranging his notes for dictation.

VI

As they settled to work Margaret was seized by an impulse. Suddenly, without thought, and in a way which surely proclaimed her the granddaughter of Charlotte Gailes, she turned to the paragon: "Would you hate to have lunch with me, Doctor? It's such a dreary day. I feel it might be cheerful to have lunch somewhere in town."

The paragon reassumed his lobster tints. Had she given the real reason for her invitation? Was it to find out if he knew more about her father? Or was this mere inconsequence? "Well, thanks very much, Mrs. Raymond. But shouldn't I—?"

"You can ask me another day."

The fog had become thick when, after midday, they left Woodside Terrace: so thick, indeed, that the slowness of the traffic in Sauchiehall Street decided them to walk. Darkness hung overhead. The long street of bright shops glowed in a blaze of light. Tramcar drivers banged their footbells impatiently. Cars, vans and taxis hooted continuously and angrily. Pavements were crowded. Yet presently as, jostling and jostled and following the paragon's large outline, she pushed her way through this cheerful, illumined discomfort, Margaret became conscious of her spirits rising, conscious of a sense of adventure. She was pleased with everything. With the haloed streetlamps, the glittering Christmas windows, even the fog; pleased with the prospect of lunching with the great striding figure who was pushing a way for her.

They sat beside a leaping fire in an Italian restaurant, making a meal of plain spaghetti, to the disappointment of a waiter who had tried to press his more elaborate ultramontane dishes upon them. Margaret chose spaghetti because she happened to like it. The paragon chose it because, as she suspected, he had no mind of his own in these things. And in a little while they, each of them, began to wonder if there were something mesmeric about this, the simplest of Italian foods. Especially if it were washed down by red wine from Tuscany beside a cheerful winter fire. When the first pangs were assuaged, they found it pleasant thoughtfully to spear the long strands of succulence, to lift them, to wind them round their forks and slowly to put them into their mouths; dreaming a little mistily of a past that was unhappy and a future that promised rosy things. And presently, as the large round flagon, its ruby contents already sunk past the level of the encasing wicker, was lifted up yet again to refill their glasses, Margaret became aware that the temperature of her friendship with the paragon had risen oddly.

Indeed, at one moment, as they talked, she found herself wondering that the doctor should find it necessary to look at her so intently; yet found herself deciding in turn that after all strong spectacles were not so bad and could even give a man an air of benevolent virility.

It was then, probably, that she had asked the paragon why he had never married. She did not really want to know. Hitherto his reasons for celibacy had left her quite incurious. Her asking released a cataract of self-revelation. The social awkwardness of short sight. The girl of his student days who had refused to look at him. His lack of self-confidence. His taking refuge in work and yet more work. The kindness of Sir James and his hopes of advancement. A young man's troubles with which she must sympathize.

But the cataract ran at last to a trickle. "I'm talking too much, Mrs. Raymond. I don't do it often, you know. But—but when a man is lonely and gets somebody like yourself to talk to—"

"It's been very interesting, Doctor. Don't apologize!" Margaret spoke briskly. The arrival of black coffee had narrowed, a little, the range of her sympathy.

He did not reply at once. Then, after a moment: "They say you're very like your father, Mrs. Raymond."

"Nonsense! My poor father was absurdly good-looking."

"Well? That's what I mean!"

Margaret was not quite certain what he meant. And refound prudence forebade her to ask. She got up. "Time to go, don't you think? I say! Look how thick the fog is getting! I'll go down to Buchanan Subway Station. That will be my best way home."

And yet as she rattled out west in the tunnel, Margaret felt grateful to her luncheon companion. She was glad she had invited him. For some three months she had been living in a world that was old and invalid. The paragon was young.

VII

That night a storm of wind and rain struck the city, reversing the weather and leaving a damp mildness.

"They tell me the fog is all blown away," Sir James said to his granddaughter as she bade him good morning. "Maggs," he went on, "I've been thinking about your next chapter. I think you should take out the car and have a look at Kinaldie this morning."

"I ought to be doing other things."

"Rubbish! What other things?"

Margaret laughed. "I'm glad I wasn't one of your nurses!"

"You would have learnt to do as you were told!"

"Do you *command* me to go to Kinaldie, Grandfather?" she asked teasing him; herself tempted after yesterday's fog by a blow in the blessed south wind and tempted, still more, by the thought of what she might find in Ayrshire.

"Aye. It's a command."

"And what am I to do when I get there?"

"I don't need to tell you."

"Impressions?"

Sir James nodded. "The feel of it. The lie of the place. What it would be like in my day."

As the car climbed up towards these moors which lie to the south of the Clyde Valley, Margaret allowed her thoughts to linger upon Sir James's people. She had taken another look at the photograph of her great-grandfather Mennock and that strange woman Constance who had become his second wife. What could that plump little man, middle-aged and merry, have found to lure him into marriage with that lean fortress of whalebone, false fringe and propriety, who stood there beside him smiling a smile that was conventionally arch and triumphantly possessive? And how—still greater wonder—did the men of Queen Victoria's day ever find courage to storm such fortresses?

What kind of people were these? But the diaries were there. The diaries of a country schoolboy and a brash, often resentful student. She must read these diligently, read between the lines.

All around her, the bog lay high and cheerless, blowing with dead heather, winter grasses and shabby marsh cotton; gashed here and there, too, by peat-cutting; the black, spongy gashes still oozing last night's rain. At times a watery sun, finding a gap in the low, moving cloud ceiling, would stab the distance with luminous slanting columns that picked out tufts and hillocks in a brilliant white light and then, as though losing interest, leave them to fade and fall back into the surrounding desolation. Moor fowl wheeled and called in the soft Atlantic wind.

And now as she turned aside full south to drop down towards the green lushness of Sir James's calf country, a mounting excitement began to take hold of her. A storyteller's excitement, it may be. A little while more and she would be in Kinaldie seeking her grandfather as he once was, seeking to find him in the stones.

She met no one who really remembered him. Nor did she try to meet anyone. They knew his name in a chemist's shop. Sir James Mennock was, of course, too important to be quite forgotten. Yes, she was told, he was born and had passed his boyhood here, had indeed, begun professional practice at Gowan Bank there, at the end of the village. Yes. Down there on the right, just before you came to the new-built houses. Or so, at least, the shop woman had heard tell. Though more than that she did not know. And, judging from her manner, did not care. But as Margaret turned away the woman called after her that she thought he was still alive and in Glasgow, though he must be an old man now. Margaret thanked her for this information and went. Fifty years is a long time for a village to remember those who have gone from it.

But she hung over the iron railing of Gowan Bank's little front garden. She walked in the mud of the main street. She stared at the old cotton mill, derelict now, but not yet pulled down. Avidly she looked at all that her grandfather must have seen and closed her eyes to the modern factory of glass and metal and to the high rows of workmen's flats, raw and newly built.

An hour of rapturous, excited prying, then she turned the car towards home. Her instinct had got all it needed. For others, Kinaldie might be a commonplace enough Ayrshire village, industrial and drab.

But in Margaret's mind the stage now stood reset. The Kinaldie of fifty years ago stood lit and waiting for the entry of a twenty-three-year-old doctor with a mop of dark-red hair.

CHAPTER EIGHT

I

On the following morning young James's stepmother sat finishing breakfast in Gowan Bank, Kinaldie. Neither her husband nor his son had yet appeared, much to her displeasure. A doctor's home, or indeed any civilized home, as Mrs. Mennock had frequently observed over the afternoon teacups to lady visitors, should, if she might so put it, run on wheels. But this lateness was not the whole of her annoyance. There were other, more serious things and she meant to speak about them.

When therefore her husband, Doctor Peter Mennock, did at last show face, she set the mood for what she had to say by pouring out his tea in a silence that was as gloomy as it was prim.

"Thanks, Connie." He took the cup. The appearance of the doctor of Kinaldie was, for a man no longer young, pleasing. His still thick hair was quite white and his clean-shaven face was pink and round. The blue of his eyes had faded to extreme paleness, now giving the plump little doctor a look of knowing inscrutability, now a look of childish candor. Neither of these looks really expressed him; but they had, together with his natural sociability, been assets in the days when he had been a not wholly mournful widower.

He looked across at his wife, then took quick refuge behind his morning newspaper. Why, he asked himself, and not for the first time, had he chosen as his second wife this woman, who, even after ten years of marriage, continued to look stiff and virginal and like nothing so much as the eternal English governess who stands, high-necked and self-sufficing, in the back row of these family groups found in the memoirs of aging European princesses?

But this was a question many people had asked themselves. How was it that this personable country doctor, with his easygoing charm and his fund of daring stories—this widower of long standing and bachelor habits, with access to the county's port and claret and, a farmer's son himself, equal access to groaning farmhouse tables—

[75]

how was it that he should have come to attach himself to this somewhat austere lady with a false fringe and gunmetal eyeglasses?

The heart of course does not give up its secrets. But for the Constance Mennocks there are such things as the rising tide of the years; the desire, before it is too late, to find some kind of male counterpart; and the suspicion that perhaps the other members of their family do not much want them. And for men like her husband, there are such things as the cooling of the blood, the wish to be done with roaming, the satisfaction of remarrying into a family with resources greater than their own; and, of course, the tepid to warm regard for that family's spinster sister, only too available and not presumably penniless.

"James not down yet?" her husband asked cheerfully, seeking to appease what he rightly took to be an angry rattling among the teacups.

"No, Peter. But I want to talk to you about him. I have a letter from Bertha this morning. She and Walter very kindly went to see him capped the other day. And they're quite sure James deliberately cut them." Bertha Lyndoch was the sister of Constance. Walter was Bertha's husband.

"What do they mean, cut them?" the question was redundant. The father, knowing something of his son's feelings, thought this deliberate cutting more than possible.

"Yes, cut! Oh, here he is. Good morning, Bruce dear." This was coldly said. The word "dear" appended to her greeting betokened self-control, not affection.

James knew this. But apart from a toneless "Good morning, Mother" he made no attempt to question or conciliate. Besides he had never become used to being called Bruce. It annoyed him anew every time he came home.

"I've decided to call you Bruce, my dear," the strange Glasgow lady, who was now going to live in the same house with himself and his father, had said to the shy, defensive country boy of thirteen on that tense occasion long ago when for the first time they had found themselves together.

"But that's not my name."

"Oh yes, it is. It's your middle name."

"But nobody calls me that."

"Well, I'm going to. I don't like Jims and Jimmies. And James is too formal. But I like Bruce. It's so short—and historical!" And here he had heard, for the first time, her strange half-scream of a laugh. "Besides, dear, if you will allow me to have my own name for you, it will make me feel that we belong a little to each other. You *will* allow me, won't you?"

Then, when he had nodded, she had bent, smelling of lavender and camphor, to press a genteel kiss upon his scowling, bashful forehead. She had meant it for the best, he had supposed. Even if he didn't like it. So she had better call him what she liked.

But he had felt he would never belong to her. He belonged to a dim, very young memory of a pale face crowned with copper hair, that had in the candlelight somewhere, somehow, bent over him, told him he was her very own and kissed him quite differently from that dry peck.

But if the new Mrs. Mennock did not have warmth enough to dispel these lingering mists of remembrance, she had in her angular way contrived to remain well enough disposed towards her husband's son. Marrying late as she had done, he was, she kept reminding herself, the only child she was ever likely to have. Thus she had tried to do what she could. And though such boyish offenses as fits of lateness at mealtimes, mud on carpets and unsavory tins of worms forgotten and found later, might not be in tune with her town-bred sense of fitness—might indeed drive her now and then to hot exasperation—yet she had not allowed them seriously to disturb her real, if sometimes much-tried, affection for the undemonstrative boy who had become her stepson.

II

Constance set about pouring out James's tea. "There you are, Bruce," she said, handing it to him. "Drink that as quickly as you can and please take your second cup for yourself. Time's getting on. I'm going through to the kitchen to take prayers. So Peggy will be wanting the teapot in a few minutes."

The link between prayers and teapots being in no way obscure to him, James thanked her and started breakfast.

Peter Mennock looked up from his newspaper. He had expected that his wife, having sown these seeds of censure, hurry and discomfort, would leave them now and go. But still she lingered. Did she first mean to lecture his son about his rudeness to her relatives?

Thus it may have been to make a diversion that the doctor said:

"You can give me another cup of tea, Connie." He pushed his teacup towards James that James in turn might continue to push it towards Connie's end of the table.

"You've had three cups already, Peter dear." She adjusted her eyeglasses on her high, narrow nose, looked brightly at her husband as though she were reproving a schoolboy prince in some royal nursery, and went on: "Isn't it time you were starting your morning visits? No, no, darling! No more tea for you!"

The little man scratched his nose crossly. His wife's use of the term "darling" seemed to him foolish and out of key. Down here in Ayrshire "darling," even at more genial moments than this one, was regarded as too fancy, too "townified," or high class or something. "I've told you I want another cup of tea," he said.

"Besides," she went on ignoring this, "I don't want you to be ill. Only yesterday, I took a little peep at your medical journal and I read that too much tea tans the membrane of your—"

"A little knowledge is a dangerous thing."

"Darling! Will you please have the politeness to let me finish what I was saying!"

"No. I want my tea."

"Very well." She did as she was bade. But she did it now as though she were the wife of a drunkard, pouring out strong drink under threat of a beating. It is possible that, in assuming this air of tragic resignation, she hoped to bring her husband to penitence. It is equally possible that, being fussy, anxious-minded and fond of Peter Mennock, she was really worried about his digestion which had, she knew, been giving him trouble lately.

But now the doctor's strategy, if strategy it had been, took effect. His wife decided that other responsibilities had better call her. She heaved a sigh of wounded dignity and said with a politeness that was intended to convey accusation: "You will excuse me, Bruce, won't you? I have my duties to attend to, even if your father chooses to neglect his. But I would like to speak to you, please, before you go out."

And the two men, knowing that no reply was expected of them, merely raised their eyes to watch her offended thinness take itself, its waspwaist and its bell skirt towards the door. Well-meaning though she might be, poor Mrs. Mennock was one of those who must ever force others into league against them.

"Did you see there was a letter for you?" the doctor asked, drawing his cup towards him and taking up his newspaper once more; reluctance to begin his day having told him falsely that there might still be some news of importance he must not miss.

"Thanks, Father. I've seen it." The envelope James now took up was bulky.

He tore it open. There was a linen handkerchief, a letter, and a check signed *H. Mackinnon Gailes.* It was written in a hand that seemed strangely out of keeping with the professor's large personality; tiny writing, with precise Greek *e*'s and small, unconceited capitals: a hand long accustomed to making notes. But the check? As he opened the sheet and read it, James felt his cheeks grow hot.

The University,
Glasgow.

DEAR DOCTOR MENNOCK,

I thank you for your letter. My daughter surprised her mother and myself very much by telling us she had spent an afternoon with a young man who was a stranger to her. Indeed, I might go so far as to say that she alarmed us. But since receiving your letter, we are now prepared to believe that you allowed this ill-advised happening out of thoughtless good nature, and merely to please a young girl possessed of more high spirits than good sense. I feel, however, that by this time your own judgment will have told you that the only thing for everyone now to do is to forget the incident as quickly as possible. I enclose a new handkerchief in place of the one you so generously destroyed to bind up my daughter's hand. I have also computed, as best I can, the amount you must have spent on her entertainment, and I enclose a check, which will, I hope, cover it. You have kindly written that you do not want any refund. But it is, of course, impossible for us to allow this. My daughter can hardly be expected to accept money from a stranger.

Yours sincerely,
H. MACKINNON GAILES

James thrust check and letter back into the envelope, crushed this into his pocket and stood up. Offended arrogance had taken the place of reason. He felt as though his face had been slapped. But, wise or foolish, so it was. The check and the last words of the letter had roused his hot, too-defensive anger. The anger of a moody, difficult young man.

Going to the window, he looked out unseeing at the little front garden of Gowan Bank. For a time he stood thus, his hands thrust deep in his pockets, staring before him. Who did Mackinnon Gailes think he, James Mennock, was? An obliging servant? Somebody's stableboy that his precious daughter had found hanging round the exhibition, that she had—oh, just for a young lady's prank of course —decided to turn into a companion for the afternoon? Someone to be thanked, paid off by Papa, and told he was no longer wanted? They needn't trouble. They couldn't want him less than he wanted to see their daughter again! Though, on consideration, it might give him some satisfaction to go to Papa and throw his check in his face!

"Well I suppose I had better get a start made," his father's voice said behind him. He heard the rustle of the newspaper as it was folded and thrown down. He turned. "All right, Jimmie? Nothing wrong?"

James managed to direct a strained smile towards him. "No. Nothing serious, anyway."

"Sure?"

James nodded.

"Good." And Peter Mennock took himself out of the room.

James watched him go, then began to move about aimlessly. The mere effort to control himself had been enough. He was a young man within whom the fires of anger flared up in a moment and again died down as quickly. Already he was searching the embers to find out what had raised them. Hurt pride? Perhaps. Ambition? He wondered.

It was difficult for James to read his own feelings. His narrow village upbringing had made him unsure, arrogant and too easily resentful. Thus he was hotly proud of the distinction gained two days ago; too conscious, now, of his worth and of a newly gained self-importance. Would the life of a country doctor always be enough?

His eyes went round his father's dining room. The ugly, varnished furniture. The gilt, commercial vases. The brass flowerpot in the window. The looped net curtains. They were all right, he supposed. But for the first time he felt the provinciality, the stuffiness of these familiar things.

[80]

On an impulse, he strode outside and slumped himself down on the garden seat set against the front of Gowan Bank. The strong morning sunlight made him frown as he sat looking about him. Painted iron railings separated the little garden from the dusty street. Here at the end of the village it was green and open. There was the church, with its graveyard, its trees and its manse. The mill manager's villa. The bank, with the business office beneath and the banker's house above. A country bank, with a tree and some grass before it.

Yet even here the sound of the spinning mill's water wheels could be heard whenever you brought accustomed ears to listen for them. Their constant, low churning made a ground bass to all the other village noises. He could hear them now, sounding beneath the chirpings of sparrows in his stepmother's rose plot, the rattle of a passing farm cart, the beating on the road of a millhand's Annan clogs. Was his life always to be dominated by that sound? Was he to live out his days as the doctor of this ugly, industrial village?

"Sir James Bruce Mennock." Who? Yes, that girl at the exhibition two days since. Rubbish, of course. The girl had just been talking for talking's sake.

He fell to thinking, about Charlotte, his rage forgotten now but with senses left awake and sharpened. The Charlotte he had met. The young girl who had come to him from nowhere. He had gone down into the exhibition that afternoon, unstrung, moody and unhappy. What had there been about her, that she had lifted the cloud? He could not tell. Yet he knew that somehow his discontent had gone. That she had turned his day of graduation into a day to remember.

IV

And now her father's letter to say that he had done wrong. James kicked the gravel beneath the garden seat. Well, had he? Shifting uneasily, running his fingers through his hair and following with his eyes the jaunty figure of a boy seated high on the rump of a great farm horse as it lumbered by on the road outside, James asked himself this question with an earnestness amounting to distress. Somehow those hours at the exhibition had become precious to him. He must not allow them to have a bitter aftertaste. He had meant no harm. Nor could he see how there had been any. It had all been so ridiculously innocent. Yet perhaps. Was he nothing after all but a country lout with no fine feelings? A rough fool, ignorant of the conventions? The reverse of the fine fellow his complacency had been painting for him?

Impatiently James got up, crossed the grass, hung over the garden railings and looked about him disconsolately. Why had he, the son of a reasonably prosperous doctor, been allowed to grow up anyhow? (Anyhow being in attendance at the Kinaldie school where he had received an excellent dominie's education, friendships with the village boys, solitary days spent hanging about the mills or roaming the countryside.) Never before had he thought of these things with resentment. But now his discontent turned upon the irresponsible father who had cared more about keeping good company himself than about teaching the ways of good company to his son. Why hadn't he, James, been sent elsewhere for his schooling as some other boys of the neighborhood had been?

Stray puffs of air were blowing dust and papers back and forth beneath the shabby trees that lined the main street of Kinaldie, a street built sometime at the end of the eighteenth century when the Industrial Revolution was new, and when water power had not for long been taught to spin and weave. Had other eyes been looking from the doctor's garden, eyes fresh to that which lay about them, they might have seen a certain dignity in this broad, well-laid-out street of workmen's houses, completed and dominated at its further end by the high cotton mill built of Ayrshire sandstone. They might have admired the worn stone stairway sweeping up between twin towers to the wide central entrance of this old place that had been built in days when craftsmen were craftsmen and could not help themselves from giving, even to such a building, a certain austere style.

But to aspects of Kinaldie, the eyes of James were blind; blinded from long habit and the uneasy thoughts now flickering and changing in his mind.

His father came out of the house, raised a hand in salute at the garden gate and went off down the street. In spite of himself, James watched his going with affection. No. It was no use criticizing that spruce, receding little figure. Widowed of his young wife and left with a child of four on his hands, what else could an amiable, rather lightweight man do than he had done? His wife's mother had come offering to take charge of his house and his child. He had accepted, gone his own way and got over his loss in his own fashion. Now, seeing it thus, James ceased blaming and began to feel sorry for his father. And a little sorry for himself, too. He had loved his grandmother, he supposed. But she had been a forceful, eccentric woman, heedless of convention. No. They had, father and son, suffered from the loss of his mother even more deeply than they knew.

He straightened himself, left the front railings and began walking up and down. These thoughts led him back to the professor's letter. It had hurt him and angered him. But he did not want to stay in his bad graces. He could not quite tell why.

Should he not take himself to Glasgow, see him face to face and apologize for his indiscretion? Prove to the man that he, James Mennock, was better than he seemed? That he was no conscienceless student, ready for any crude adventure? Pacing back and forth, his eyes on the grass, his hands still plunged in his pockets, rightly or wrongly James felt himself drawn to this proposal he had just made to himself.

But presently, hearing her call him, he turned to see his stepmother standing in the sunlight at the front door of Gowan Bank.

V

Constance Mennock emerged from the kitchen where she had been holding prayers with her little maid Peggy and the doctor's stableboy and gardener, Davie. If she had been asked why she did so every morning, she would probably have replied that "Well, the doctor wouldn't do it so somebody had to." But if, following upon this, she had been asked: "And why does somebody have to?" this question would have brought her reasoning to a halt or at best to a defensive: "Well, why not?" For she was not a particularly devout woman, nor was she particularly interested in the immortal souls of her two young servants.

But Mrs. Mennock, in her gropings towards the light, was a conformist. She liked to feel she was doing what others thought right; to feel, moreover, that these others were holding her up as a model of rightness. She liked to think that the village people told each other that if anything on earth was certain it was that no nonsense went on in the doctor's house. Which was indeed true, if one took nonsense to mean what Mrs. Mennock meant by it.

And so it came about that every morning a rosy little country girl washed her plump, red hands at the scullery sink and sat down at the kitchen table opposite a raw and somewhat sulky male creature of nineteen or twenty, reading a chapter with him from the little Bibles they had each been given by their mistress, who stood over them, following and now and then pronouncing rightly their stumbling, bashful words.

Once an exasperated and more than usually stumbling Davie, suffering much correction, had looked up at his tormentor, red-faced and driven, and exclaimed: "When ye check me ye pit me ott!" But this lapse of temper, so kind and firm had Mrs. Mennock been, was never repeated.

Then, when the ordeal of the chapter reading was over, the couple bent much-relieved heads while their preceptress, joining her hands and closing her eyes behind her gunmetal eye clips, stood like some reverent, long-necked bird and offered a bright intercession to their Maker. The prayer had long ago settled into what was to all intents a set piece, the blessings interceded for being much the same each morning, since, as Mrs. Mennock was not very inventive, it was difficult to keep on thinking of new blessings.

Thereafter she would open her eyes, allow for a pious pause, then say: "Now you can have your cup of tea. But time is precious, remember. Go and get the dining room teapot, Peggy, and just put some hot water into it. That should be quite strong enough for both of you," and go out of the kitchen, smiling her genteel, detached smile.

And even if Peggy should smirk, or perhaps even wink at Davie, as she reached up to the mantelpiece for the coronation tea box, ornamented with the portraits of the new King Edward and the new Queen Alexandra and help herself to forbidden tea; even if Davie should sniff, suck his teeth audibly and shrug as though to say: "That's what folks like me and you is forced to pit up wi'," yet who shall say that the morning ritual at Gowan Bank was anything but good?

"Father gone, Bruce?" From the doorstep she addressed her stepson with her habitual brightness. The little brush she had had with his father about too much tea drinking was all forgotten now. Hers, indeed, was not a mind that liked to harbor grievance. Though this morning she could not dismiss from it her grievance against James.

"Yes. There he is. Down at the end of the street, Mother. Look. Not far from the mill gates."

"I can't come out, Bruce. Not in my working apron. What would people think if they saw the doctor's wife outside looking like this?"

She was now wearing an apron of grey alpaca which, however, she had contrived to make amateurishly frilly. In one hand she held a feather brush and in the other a duster. Her manner of holding these things was offhand and refined as though, lacking knowledge of their use but having a vague idea they had some connection with the parlormaid, she was merely about to hand them over.

"You look all right to me, Mother."

"That's because you're a man. Men don't understand the finer shades."

"Shades of what?" James was not above teasing her now and then.

"Shades of right behavior, Bruce. What a lady should do, and what she should not do."

"I see."

"Your father must be going into the Regans if he's down there. These Irish millhands are dreadful about paying. The Regans must be owing us I don't know how much! See if he is, Bruce."

"I can't see him now."

"There you are! Didn't I tell you? That's where he's gone!"

"The poor lady will be going to have another bairn, Mother. How many will that make now? Twelve or thirteen?"

Mrs. Mennock's face became regally blank. For those who knew the finer shades there was no such thing as unborn babies. Not even under gooseberry bushes. Except to husbands, maybe. Certainly not to stepsons. Even medical ones. But now her look changed to severity. "Bruce," she said, "there's something I want to say to you."

"Right, Mother. Fire ahead."

"No, Bruce. This is a serious matter. Come inside, please."

VI

Constance led the way into the doctor's consulting room, a drab little room at the back of the house with a view of the coalhouse and the meat safe. It was here, in his younger days, that she had always brought him for reprimand. Now, remembering this and looking round at the familiar things—at the little-used and out-of-date equipment, at the row of bottles with their glass stoppers, containing heaven knew what, at the wall chart of a sexless human body, at the long examination sofa with the mended rent in the horsehair, at the case of old medical books, most of which Peter Mennock had used as a student—James wondered what was coming.

"Well, Mother?"

She closed the door, threw her feather brush and duster into a corner, then sat down on the edge of the sofa and clasping her hands in front of her. "Bruce," she said, "this morning I had a letter from your Aunt Bertha that has hurt me."

"What did Mrs. Lyndoch say?" For reasons undefined even to himself, James had up to now refused to call these genial people "aunt" and "uncle."

Constance produced the letter from the pocket of her alpaca apron. It was folded at the place she wanted. She began to read. "'What a beautiful day for James' capping. We were very surprised that neither you nor Peter were there. Distinction too! Peter must be proud! What a clever boy! And very grand he looked in his gown and everything! I'm glad that we at least saw him. Walter came out specially from town to take me to the Bute Hall.'" Here Mrs. Mennock raised her eyes, looked at James accusingly, then went on: "'But why did he run away from us? He knew we were there, for before the ceremony he caught sight of us in the distance and waved. He must have known we had come for nobody's sake but his own. Walter was, to say the least, most disappointed. You know how he loves what he calls a "do." He had it planned that James, and you and Peter if you came, were all to come into town with us and, as he put it, "have the lunch of your lives!" Have we offended James in some way? We can't understand it.'" Here Mrs. Mennock stopped. Even her fingers, as she slowly folded up the letter, managed to convey how hurt she was. "Well?" she asked at length, her eyes still upon her folding. And as he did not answer she added: "And they say you saw them!"

It would have been easy for a different kind of young man to claim that he had not; that he had been waving to someone else. But James being James, found himself responding with an embarrassed "Aye." He had turned, gone to the window and was standing looking uncomfortably at the meat safe. He knew how his stepmother reverenced the Lyndochs, looked up to them in all things, drew her importance, her sense of superiority here in the village from them.

Yet what was there to say? How could he begin to tell her that he had gone to his graduation ceremony unhappy and heartsore? How could he tell her of Mrs. Lermont's letter; a letter from a woman she had always referred to as his "Glasgow landlady," her narrow, genteel understanding unable to grasp that this woman was James' friend? He remembered how, on the one occasion he had brought young Lermont down here to Kinaldie, she had been detached and patronizing, and how he had judged it best not to bring him again. What could he say to this stepmother with whom he found so little contact?

But now the room was silent behind him. So silent that the stillness forced itself upon him; forced him to turn round. He was amazed to find Constance sitting, her eyeglasses laid aside, weeping noiselessly into her handkerchief.

"Mother!" Ashamed and at a loss, he crossed and stood beside her. He saw her viewpoint plainly enough and the justice of her accusation. Why were his emotions, his feelings tied in knots within him? Why must he be so inarticulate? "Mother, what is it?"

She raised her face from her handkerchief and looked about the room unhappily, avoiding his eyes. "I've tried with you, Bruce. Tried ever since I came to this house. But sometimes I think—" Tears stopped her here but immediately she went on: "I know I'm not clever. Yet I tried to fill your mother's place as best I could. But I've never understood you. Why, for instance, haven't you gone much more to Bertha and Walter's house all those years you were in Glasgow? You knew their door was open to you. And now you think nothing of openly cutting them when they take the trouble to go to your capping!"

"I'm sorry, Mother. What would you like me to do?"

"What can you do?" She picked up her glasses and began wiping them.

"How would it be if I went to see the Lyndochs?"

"What? Go to Glasgow?"

"Why not? I'll tell them I wasn't in very good shape and apologize. Would that please you?"

She thought of this for a time without replying. But now he could see by her face that he had already made his peace with her. Anxious to justify her, he was glad to remind himself that she was quick to forgive. "Well? What do you think, Mother?"

She nodded. "I think they would like that, dear." She stood up. "Oh, perhaps I've made too much of this, but—"

"No, Mother. It was my fault. I should have spoken to them."

"You're a good boy after all, Bruce."

[87]

Emotion hung in the air between them. But habit would not allow either to express it. They could only stand there together, woodenly pleased.

"I'll go to see them very soon. Tomorrow, maybe." His anxiety to put things right was real.

But now this storm, blowing over, had also fixed another decision for him. Being in Glasgow, he could try at the same time to see Professor Mackinnon Gailes. And the sooner the better.

Constance Mennock had come back to normal. It was her way to dismiss uncomfortable emotion as quickly as she could. Now she was looking about her for the brush and the duster. When she spoke, her voice had resumed that baffling note of impersonality that had ever been death to intimacy between her stepson and herself. "That would be splendid, dear! Where can I have put—? Oh, there they are. Now I must go upstairs and see Peggy properly started. I'm late as it is, and this is drawing room morning."

CHAPTER NINE

I

Professor Mackinnon Gailes had been forced to do more running about than he cared for on a warm morning. His wife had sent him to the agency to pick up and pay for those bewildering little books of travel tickets and to make sure of train times. She had also sent him to her milliner's.

"But look here, Edie, I can't go into a hat shop!"

"I don't see why not."

"I wouldn't know what to say to the young women."

"Then I'll tell you what to say, Henry. Say, 'Please, can you have the new hat for Mrs. Mackinnon Gailes that was being altered and was to be ready today.'"

"Couldn't you—?"

"No. I've got too much to do. For one thing, I have to pack for everybody. And if you want to get to Switzerland at all—"

"I never said I wanted to get to Switzerland. It was your idea."

"Don't you want your daughter to be educated?"

"Oh, very well. I'll go. I'll go."

But it had been an exhausting business. And now, with lunch behind him and with the pleasant coolness of armchair leather about him, he sat in his study drowsily assuring himself that east, west, home, after all, was best, and that it was a pity anyone should ever feel the need to leave it.

Presently, as he was sitting on the summit of the Matterhorn with his daughter Charlotte, explaining this truth to her, he became aware of the rattle of his door handle, then heard the door itself swing upon its hinges. He reopened his eyes reluctantly.

A large young man with a pale face and untidy dark-red hair was standing, hat in hand, looking down upon him.

The professor resented this. He wanted to be left alone. For an instant he wondered if it might not be possible to close his eyes again and return to the top of the Matterhorn. But who *was* this young man? And how had he got in?

Now he was up and standing on the mat before the empty fireplace, large and leonine, his legs planted apart, his hands behind his back, examining this intruder who stood waiting, neither overconfident nor abashed.

"Well?" he asked at length. "And how did *you* get here?"

"I was told I could come back."

"Back? Who told you that?"

"A lady who looked like your wife, sir."

"But why didn't she tell me?"

"She must have forgotten."

"Well, she had no right to forget!"

James Mennock felt he could hardly discuss this, so confined himself to saying: "You werena here when I came about twelve this morning, sir. She told me on the doorstep."

For a time the professor looked gloomily at his feet without replying, then he muttered: "No, I wasn't here," into his beard. Suddenly he looked up, fixing James with the avenging eye of a prophet. "Who let you in?"

"A woman, sir."

"The house is upside down! These cleaners don't know the rules! Where have all the maids gone?"

"I couldna say, sir."

"Packing to go for their own holidays, most likely."

As there was nothing to reply to this, James waited.

Again the professor fixed him with his eye. "Well? Why are you here? What's your name?"

"I got a letter from you yesterday, Professor Gailes. My name is James Mennock." Then, having got himself thus far, James added: "You sent me a check, and I've brought it back."

The elder man's bushy eyebrows rose with surprise at this, but whether the eyes beneath them were now kindled with interest, amusement or anger the young man could not tell.

"Look here, you had better sit down."

"Thanks, sir, I'll stand."

"I don't want that check back, Mennock."

"And I don't want to keep it, Professor Gailes."

"Then what are we going to do?"

As a reply to this, Mennock withdrew the professor's letter from his pocket, unfolded it, detached the check, slowly tore it into pieces and laid the pieces on the table.

The other watched him with curiosity. "Now, why did you do that?" he asked.

"I told you I didna want it."

"We don't like the idea of your paying for our daughter's entertainment."

"And I don't like the idea of being paid off as if I was her flunky, sir!"

The professor considered this. Yes. He supposed a young man might feel like that. It was difficult. He wished his wife were here to decide for him. Edie always knew what to think.

Now James, prompted perhaps by the professor's look of perplexity, found himself insisting: "But surely there wasna any harm in what I did, sir."

"No, no, Mennock! I daresay not. No, of course not."

"I told Miss Gailes I would write to you."

"Yes, yes, of course you did."

"And you can see for yourself," James added artlessly, "that I am quite respectable, sir."

"Yes. Oh, yes. Quite, Mennock. Very respectable, I should say. I've no reason—no reason at all, really, to doubt that."

The professor shuffled uneasily. No. He was no good at this kind of thing. Edie could do so much better. Why was she upstairs packing? Respectable? Yes. Take that point now. Well? How could he possibly tell if this young man *were* respectable? Even if he had just assured him he was certain about it? And yet if you looked at him—no. Mennock certainly didn't look like a bad hat. The professor came to a halt here. What was he to do about this young man? It would be so much easier to leave things at that. But then, he would have to report to Edie. And what would he have to say? That he had stood smiling, while his disconcertingly firm visitor tore up his check and thanked the visitor for doing so, then had led the visitor to the door and bade him a genial goodbye? He pulled himself together. "My wife and I were very upset over this exhibition escapade of yours with my daughter, Mr. Mennock," he said, hoping he had put enough outrage into his voice.

"Doctor Mennock, sir."

"Doctor Mennock. I beg your pardon."

"Do I look like a rascal, sir?"

"No, Doctor Mennock, no." And then, as he could think of nothing effective to follow this, he stroked his beard and tried to change the subject. "Charlotte told us you had just graduated."

But James did not reply to this. "I knew you would think my behavior queer, sir. That's why I wrote to you at once," he said.

"Very good of you. But why the escapade at all?"

Remembrance of a dazzle of sunshine, of feelings of release, of two hours of gay irresponsibility came to James. But these, he felt, would perhaps make bad points of argument. They could not tell with the professor. Instead he allowed his face to break into a smile. "The wee lassie would have been vexed with me if I hadna, Professor. And as far as respectability was concerned, she might have been spending a couple of hours in the charge of a policeman."

"Yes, yes. Quite, Doctor Mennock. But—" Really what could one say to this kind of thing? The professor was desperate.

It was with a sense of deep relief that again he heard the study door handle turn.

Charlotte burst into the room. "Father," she said. "Mother says you must go up to her and decide once and for all what you want packed. Oh—I didn't know—"

"Of course, yes. I'll go up now." And the professor was gone, the idea of escape having wiped all else from his mind.

II

It was a moment before Charlotte grasped it was James who was standing there in the room.

"Miss Gailes."

"Doctor Mennock!"

"You didna expect to see *me*." He looked down at the young hand that was now stretched out to take his own. "Hand better?"

"Yes, thanks." She had backed away from him shyly. There was little now of the young woman in her manner. She was a self-conscious child.

"Or did you know I was here?" he asked.

"No." Her eyes turned towards the door. "Well, I had better go, I think." She began to move.

"No. Wait." These two words had, it seemed, come from him of their own accord. James wondered why. She was a queer girl this. Confident one day. Timid the next. "Are we not to be friends then?"

he asked as she stood waiting. "You said we were to be friends the last time I saw you."

She merely looked at him unhappily.

"Well?"

"Mother and Father didn't like it."

"They know very well there was nothing wrong with it."

"Of course they knew there was nothing wrong in it!" As she said this he was surprised by the heat of her tone, by her sulky look, by the flash of rebellion.

"I've been talking to your father. I tore up his check. That's it there." He indicated the remains on the table.

"Tore it up? But why?"

"Never mind. But remember, Miss Gailes, I paid for our day at the exhibition, and nobody else is going to pay for it."

She said nothing to this. Now she watched his long fingers collecting, mechanically, the torn pieces and stuffing them into a pocket. For a time there was silence.

"Are you sorry I paid for you?"

She hesitated, and for some reason unexplained, her eyes, as she raised them to his, shone with tears. Then she said, "No" quite simply and once more held out her hand. "I must help Mother to pack. We're leaving here tomorrow."

Again James was surprised to find himself saying: "I don't want you to go without promising to be friends with me."

A tear had rolled down either cheek now. But James could not guess at the emotion behind them.

"How can we be friends? We won't see each other, perhaps for months. My parents mean to leave me in Lausanne."

"But we can be friends, even if you don't see me. You can still say to yourself that a big, red-haired yokel called James Mennock is your friend."

For an instant she stood, seeming to ponder his words. Then, quite suddenly, her smile broke. And now, though her eyes still glistened, they were wide with mischief. "It isn't a nasty red," she said. "It's a very nice red. I told you I had no intention of losing sight of you. Goodbye, Doctor Mennock."

Once again he moved to stop her, but this time she was gone.

"I'm sorry to bring you up, Henry." Edith, who had been bending over a trunk, straightened herself to say this to her husband as he arrived, flushed and panting from the effort of bringing his large person upstairs. "But I really had to be certain what clothes you wanted to take. Were you—" she found the word "asleep" on the tip of her tongue but, knowing that this would offend, managed just in time to substitute—" 'working?' "

"No. I wasn't." The professor ran his fingers through his mane. "Young Mennock was downstairs."

"Mennock? You mean the young man that Charlotte—? The young man we wrote the letter to? Was he the person I saw this morning?"

Her husband nodded. "Must have been."

"Is he here? In this house? Whatever for?"

The professor looked sheepish. "He won't accept my check."

"But why, Henry? Is he angry?"

"I don't know what he is, Edie. No. I don't think angry, exactly."

This was ridiculous. "But why didn't you insist?"

"He tore it to pieces."

"Then he *must* have been angry."

"No. I wouldn't say angry."

"Really, Henry, you're quite impossible! How did it all end? What did he say before you showed him out?"

"I've told you. And I didn't show him out. He's still downstairs."

"What? Downstairs in your study?"

"Yes, you see, Edie, when Charlotte—"

"Henry! Is Charlotte downstairs with him?"

"No. Here she is!" He was much relieved by the sight of his daughter just at this moment. It rescued him from at least some of her mother's displeasure.

Edith looked at Charlotte critically. The girl was flushed, but that could have come from bounding first down and then upstairs again. The child's appearance told her nothing. Edith decided it was safest to be crisp. "Your father tells me Doctor Mennock was here, darling," she said. "Had he gone when you got downstairs?"

"No. Why?"

"I didn't know if he was still here. That's all. Did you speak to him?"

"Yes, of course! He's a great friend of mine! I've told you that before."

Her mother flinched but pretended to be amused. "Rubbish, darling! How can you say anyone is a great friend when you've only seen him once before?"

"But he is! He's the most wonderful young man I know!"

Edith took a tight hold. It would be folly, she felt, to be severe. Her smile became wholesomely bright. "You know so many wonderful young men, don't you?" But was the unwanted visitor still in the house? If he were, she had better go down, see him for herself and deal with him. She hated this necessity. But duty was duty. And Henry could be so helpless! "But is the poor young man left high and dry in the study?" she asked, artfully concerned.

Charlotte looked distressed. "Well, yes. I think he must be, Mother."

"But how rude of you both!" She stopped to look at father and daughter. "I must go down and speak to him."

Charlotte's distress increased. "I'll rush down and apologize!" She was poised for flight.

But her mother just managed to stop her. "No, Charlotte! Indeed not! It's not for little girls to do the honors of this house."

Edith took a hasty look at herself in her husband's dressing room mirror, regretted her slight untidiness, and decided ruefully that she did not look quite so like the Sargent as she might have wished. But she must hurry downstairs at once, before her daughter or her husband found new ways of making things yet more difficult.

IV

James, having waited uncertainly in the study for a time, was just deciding that all he could now do was to take himself out of the house when the distinguished, rather formidable woman he had already seen for an instant that morning came into the room.

"Doctor Mennock! What rude people you must think us in this house!" Her expression had been severe as she entered, but now she was smiling conventionally. She held out her hand.

"It's all right. I was just going away," James said as he took it.

"But how dreadful to let you creep out like a burglar! I had no idea there was anybody with my husband when I called him away. You must forgive him. I'm afraid he can be such a very vague person.

Is there any message you would like me to take to him? Or had you quite finished your business?"

"Quite finished, Mrs. Mackinnon Gailes, thanks." Then, hoping to establish sympathy, James added: "Miss Gailes was here for a minute. I'm glad her hand's all right again."

"I know it's early for tea, Doctor Mennock, but you must let me ring for something just before you go. It's so warm today! Some lemonade? Or I think, perhaps, my husband may have some whisky here in his cupboard?"

"No, thanks." This woman, he saw, did not like him, and the knowledge somehow prompted him to say: "Professor Mackinnon Gailes sent me a check for what I had spent on Miss Gailes at the exhibition the other day. But I didna want to be paid."

Her smile was still empty. "I'm afraid I'm very stupid about business things, Doctor Mennock. But I daresay you arranged all that with my husband."

Her smile and her determined deafness before all direct allusion to his meeting with Charlotte angered him. And yet he felt he must still, even a little desperately, even with some self-abasement, try to reach her sympathy. "It was very kind of Miss Gailes to make friends with me at the exhibition, Mrs. Mackinnon Gailes. I know I was in the wrong to let her. But I was lonely. And it was all right. Honest it was."

Still the smile. "The exhibition is great fun, isn't it?" She was holding out her hand. "Well, perhaps, if there's nothing more— Did you leave your hat in the hall, Doctor Mennock?"

He went scarlet to the hair as he forced himself to take the hand of Charlotte's mother and turned to quit the room. He had no weapon to match this bright unkindness other than a blunt coarseness. And that he would not use.

"Oh, that's your hat is it? Good. Can you open the door for yourself, Doctor Mennock?"

In moments of stress, James's accent broadened. Now, in addition, it was redolent of disgust. "Aye," he said. "Oh, don't think I canna open yer door, Mrs. Gailes!"

For an instant Edith halted at the foot of the stairs. No. She had not relished this. Indeed it had quite shaken her. But with Henry so hopeless about things like that, what else was there to do? Someone had to send that pushing young Ayrshireman about his business.

V

It was about six o'clock when James, hot, tired and still smoldering at the treatment he had received at the hands of Charlotte's mother, presented himself at the home of his stepmother's sister.

Walter and Bertha Lyndoch lived in Huntly Gardens, one of the best garden squares in the west of the city. It lay on a slope and was stepped into several descending levels of wide green lawn, each level broken by handsome flower beds and clumps of rhododendron. Blossoming trees made a glory of the Gardens in the springtime.

But although they lived in this garden square of handsome houses, the Lyndochs were not quite of it. Huntly Gardens was a stronghold of the conventions. Here, although the exhaust pipe of the motor car had already begun to puff its vulgar fumes into the air of the twentieth century, were families of standing who still retained their shining carriages and their Victorian importance.

Bertha and her husband struck a different note. Their high, airy house on the north side was reported to be "queer" or "modern" by the gentlemen of the Gardens Committee at such times as it was Walter's turn to receive them in it; such times being, indeed, the only times of contact the Gardens much cared to have with the Lyndochs. On their return home these gentlemen, having hung up their hats in their own yellow pine cloakrooms and having refreshed their eyes with the tassels and velvets of their own late Victorian drawing rooms, would smugly assure their complacent wives—and not, perhaps, quite so complacent daughters—that it was after all only the good, solid, old-fashioned things that could give a house any real appearance; not the pale shades and new-fangled emptiness to be found in the house they had just quitted. At which the ladies, agreeing but consumed with curiosity, would wonder if they might not —without telling their lords and masters, of course—dare to bow to Mrs. Lyndoch as she passed down the Gardens, as a preliminary to paying her a condescending but inquisitive afternoon call.

Not that there was anything disreputable about these people James had come to visit. Far from it. Walter Lyndoch was much too rich to be disreputable. It was known that he was the owner of a factory—no one knew its products—somewhere in the East End. A factory which must run by itself, surely, if one thought of the number of times its owner's name could be found on catalogues and programs, as a sponsor and promotor of the city's art and music. And

Mrs. Lyndoch had, by hearsay and by the competent sounds coming from her drawing room window when it happened to be open, as it was this afternoon, an unusual talent for music and was said to have studied abroad. But would any lady play with such loud effectiveness, the Gardens asked itself, if she had not at some time been obliged to let herself be heard, and seen, in public places? And thus, as a dreadful corollary, been obliged to stoop to accepting money for so doing? The Gardens doubted it. No. Better leave the Lyndochs to their own informal friends. They were, the Gardens had long since decided, rather too arty.

The piano was thundering as a parlormaid threw open the door for James and withdrew, leaving him standing in a cool room of grey and lavender spaciousness, of polished wood and rugs, now pleasantly thrown into a luminous twilight by the deep sun awnings outside the windows. For a moment longer the thunder continued, but presently the thunderer became aware of him, dropped her hands and came forward, a robust, middle-aged figure in easy summer clothes of Liberty silk.

"James! I'm sorry. Have I been keeping you standing?" She pressed his hand with a pianist's strong fingers.

"No. I've just come in."

"You look hot."

"Yes, it's hot."

"Well anyway, it's cool in here." Bertha Lyndoch was firmly confident and seldom at a loss. It was her habit to affect a cheerful brusqueness. But her sister's stepson now stood looking so ruffled, so sheepish, that even she found it difficult to think what next to say.

But James at once solved this problem for her. "Mrs. Lyndoch, I'm sorry for what I did at the capping the other day."

"Determined to apologize at once and get it over? Is that it, James? But not Mrs. Lyndoch. Aunt Bertha, please. Haven't I told you already? Yes. Your uncle and I were very angry with you. What have you got to say for yourself?"

Though she had been with her sister now and then at Kinaldie, James knew her so little that he was uncertain if she were angry or merely teasing. But he answered simply: "I was put out about something. I had a great friend. He should have been there too. But he had died."

As he said no more, Bertha rightly concluded he did not want to. Her voice had lost its brusqueness as she answered: "I see. I'm sorry about that, James." Then after a moment: "All the same, if you could come to be capped, you could come and speak to your Uncle Walter and me." Then, as he continued tongue-tied, "Well, go and wash your face in cold water to cool yourself, and we'll say no more about it. I'll have something for you to drink when you come back."

This was talk in an idiom James understood perfectly. He went as he was told, knowing he was forgiven.

VI

Refreshed by cold water, James began to feel better. On leaving the professor's house he had spent some hours in the sunshine—he could not have told where—wandering in sultry streets, sitting on dusty park benches, angry and miserable. Edith Gailes's treatment of him tore at his stiff pride. How, he had asked himself, could he now go to the Lyndochs and make his apologies? He had done enough of that for one day; enough of cringing and self-abasement. But at last reason had won and here he was.

Back in the shaded music room, he found Bertha bending over a large crystal bowl filled with a Rhine wine mixture upon which floated pieces of fresh fruit and ice.

"Oh, hullo, James! You look cooler and, I must say, cleaner. Some of this? It's stronger than it looks. I learnt to make it when I was a student in Dresden more years ago than anybody has any business to ask me. Your Uncle Walter likes it on these hot nights. He should be here any time now."

James accepted the cold, misted glass from her hands and its cool, unexpected strength increased his sense of betterment. How, he asked himself, was it possible for his stepmother Constance to have come out of the same nest as this good-natured, pleasantly eccentric, self-assured woman?

As though she had read his thoughts, Bertha asked: "How's Connie?"

"All right, I think, Mrs.—"

"Don't you dare!"

"Aunt Bertha."

"That's better!" She turned towards the windows, glass in hand, as she went on: "Scrubbing and polishing and fussing about as usual?"

"Well—" James stopped to smile. She seemed to know her sister.

[99]

Bertha turned round to look at him. "Be nice to Connie, James. She's happier now with your father than ever she's been. I know. She's told me. I had all the money spent on me. I was expected to be a musical wonder. Connie was left at home to be our parents' nurse. Be nice to her. Even if—well, anyway—be nice to her. She deserves it."

"I always try to be, Aunt Bertha," James said, her earnestness and the contents of the crystal bowl turning aside for him any doubts about his own truthfulness.

"That's a good boy." She began to pace the room again. "I see you're looking at the new picture. Do you like it? It's difficult to see it in this shaded light."

James was looking at the only picture in the room, a monster canvas in fresh, oddly applied colors by the Glasgow painter Hornel that almost filled one wall. It showed a group of pinafored little girls crouching to pick primroses and wild hyacinths beneath a tangle of flowering blackthorn.

"Well?"

James was cautious. "It's very bright," he said.

She laughed. "I've been wondering. Your uncle gave it to me for my I-won't-tell-you-which birthday. Don't say I said so, but he was really giving it to himself. He was looking for an excuse to spend so much money. And the excuse, as usual, had to be me. All his friends were buying Hornels and of course he had to have one too. It's very modern, isn't it?"

"Yes. Very."

Then as neither she nor James were able to think of anything more to say about it, Bertha held out her hand for James's glass. "More?"

He gave it to her, then drew out his handkerchief to dry hands that were damp from the misting on his glass. In doing this, fragments of the torn check fell upon the floor.

"Hullo. Been tearing up good money?"

He bent down to collect the pieces, feeling foolish. "It's a check somebody sent me. I dinna want it."

"And why, now, didna you want it, James?" she asked, echoing a little his country voice.

His face was red and sulky as he straightened himself to take back the filled glass from her hands.

Was he resenting her light mimicry of his speech, she wondered?

"That's Professor Henry Mackinnon Gailes's check," he said angrily. "And I tore it up under his nose, if you would like to know!"

Bertha Lyndoch took her own way with his outburst. She smiled.

"Well, you're telling me whether I would like to know or not, aren't you James?" she said. "I've never met the professor, but if it's any comfort to you, I hate his wife." This was not quite true. Bertha was too easy, too self-confident to hate anybody very much, but it was her way of showing sympathy, of putting herself on James's side. "She wrote asking me as a favor to hear her daughter's playing and to tell her if I thought the girl was worth an expensive teacher. She's being sent to Lausanne, it seems."

James looked up. "And what did you say about it?"

"I've heard worse. They can afford expensive teachers, so what does it matter?"

"Why did you hate Mrs. Gailes, Aunt Bertha?"

"Can't stand her kind. Hoity-toity. Mrs. Gailes seemed to think she was doing me an honor by bringing her girl here."

"Abominable woman!"

Why this violence? Bertha looked at him. James had the wounded look of an unhappy child. "Sit down, James, and tell me about this."

Which James did. Finding a sudden, unexpected release in being able to confide in this forthright yet not insensitive woman, against whom until now he had been so prejudiced.

Knowing James's background, the story of his meeting with Charlotte at the exhibition delighted his listener. He had of course acted, if not wrongly, at least highly unconventionally. But now in her new-found role of confidante to her sister's stepson, Bertha knew she dare not say this. "No, James, I can see that her majesty wouldn't at all like her daughter to be hobnobbing with strange young men! Well? And what then?"

The exchange of letters. The check. This afternoon's encounter.

An amusing story of brash behavior. Yet Bertha was moved by it. And heart, if not head, took sides with James. For her the ranks had closed. She could see Edith Gailes's cold dismissal of this inexperienced, vulnerable boy. And she resented it. What right had the Mackinnon Gailes family to treat James like this—offhandedly and with scorn? James was going to count for something. One day they might be sorry.

She got up and began to pace about again.

"Have you told Connie about this?" she asked him presently.

He shook his head.

No. Her sister was not of the stuff from which confidantes were made. "Well, I'm glad you've told me. Oh—better forget all about it."

"Yes. I suppose so."

But a sudden confidence and a resentment shared may, added together, mean the beginning of a friendship. And a new friendship is a warming thing.

As she turned in her pacing, Bertha saw that already her guest looked happier from having unburdened himself. "James," she said impulsively, "I've just been thinking. You've been Connie's stepson for years now, yet for some reason Walter and I have never got to know you. I wish you would come to see us when you come back to Glasgow. Will you do that?"

And borne upon the same wave of goodwill James answered: "Thanks, Aunt Bertha. Yes. I'll come."

"Good boy."

A breath of evening coolness stirred the striped awnings and came through the open window. Steps familiar to Bertha could be heard coming up the Gardens. She went to look out. "There's your Uncle Walter," she said. "Now we can think about dinner."

CHAPTER TEN

I

Seeing him from her place behind the breakfast cups, Constance Mennock rose, went to her front doorstep and stood watching the advance of the postman over the top of her gunmetal eye clips. "Beautiful morning, Willie. The end of the first week in August already and never a sign of the weather breaking!" Her high-pitched voice was bracingly bright as she held out her hand for the letters.

"It's far over dry," the man answered unamiably.

"How can it be too dry? Just think how wonderful for the exhibition!"

The man grunted. Why should he, a serious-minded Ayrshireman and a church elder, be required to think of anything so frivolous and far away as the Glasgow exhibition? "They're sayin' the corn'll be short on the stalk an' licht in the ear, if there's nae rain," he said.

"Still, Willie, just for this year! When it's *so* important for the exhibition!"

Her and her exhibitions! "That's a' there is for you," he said, turning on his heel and making for the garden gate.

"Thank you, Willie. Thank you, indeed!" Constance called happily after him, determined to show she had taken no umbrage.

She stood for a moment in the sunshine examining what he had given her before she went inside. Two bills. She knew about these. A circular from a firm of medical suppliers. And a postcard. Constance adjusted her eyeglasses and looked at the picture. Isola Bella, Maggiore. Delightful! Perhaps one day, she and Peter— But who could be sending them a postcard from Lake Maggiore? She turned the card over. "Doctor James Mennock." Bruce? Who could—? For a moment she struggled, but curiosity won. Yes. Why, indeed, shouldn't she read it? People didn't, after all, write secrets on postcards.

Arrived two days ago. Mother insisted on coming. Was brought to Stresa by my grandfather or somebody when young, and has

[103]

dreamed about its beauty ever since. All Father and I can dream about is heat, so are leaving for coolest mountain top in Switzerland tomorrow. Shall write again soon.

CHARLOTTE.

Charlotte? Now who on earth could this Charlotte be, that she should go traveling with her parents to North Italy and send back postcards to Bruce of all people? Bruce, who so far as she knew had never yet looked at a girl! With a smile and a genteel clearing of the throat, Constance returned to the dining room. Well really! Fancy Bruce with a young lady.

"Any letters, Connie?" Peter Mennock asked.

She became magnificently offhand. "Two bills and a circular. Nothing, really. Oh, and this postcard for you, Bruce."

Settling down in her place once more, Constance watched him as he examined the picture, read what the mysterious Charlotte had written, examined the Isola Bella once more, then laid it down. How tiresome of him not to say anything about it.

"Did I see a foreign stamp on that postcard, Bruce dear?" she asked, unable in the end to contain herself.

"Yes. Italian."

"Some friend traveling in Italy?"

"That's right."

Well really! Why couldn't he say? But she must try again. "May I see the picture? I love foreign postcards! Especially from Italy."

He gave it to her.

"Maggiore! Wonderful!" And as he continued to make no comment: "I wonder if it's hot down there just now? I should think it would be, when it's so hot even in this cold country. Doesn't your friend say?" She returned the card to him.

But James merely said: "Thanks," and put it into his pocket.

Constance gulped down her exasperation with the remainder of her tea, then stood up. "Well," she said. "Time for kitchen prayers. More tea, anybody? In a minute I'll be sending Peggy for the teapot, remember." Then as no one had the politeness to reply to this, she smiled mistily, shook her head in gentle reprimand and went off down the kitchen passage thoughtfully humming "By Cool Siloam's Shady Rill," to show she could keep her temper. No, indeed! Far be it from her even to think of anything that was not her business! Besides, sooner or later, she would be sure to hear.

James drew the postcard once again from his pocket, rereading it and lingering over the picture. It would have been hard for him to say what he felt about Charlotte at this time. Had he never gone to her father's house; had he seen nothing of her after leaving her on that first afternoon at the exhibition entrance, it is possible that she would have gone from his mind.

But her mother's treatment of him had stung, and continued to sting his pride. And this stinging, while it kept reminding him of an unpleasant woman, did in the end always bring him back to the fact that this woman had a daughter who was *not* unpleasant. Charlotte continued to hang luminous and insistent, gentle and mischievous, in James's mind.

But this postcard? Did she mean to start a correspondence? No. That was too childish, too irresponsible. He had meant nothing like that when he had talked to her of friendship. He had, he supposed, only been asking for her goodwill. Writing letters to a schoolgirl who could never be anything to him, whose parents had shown their disapproval of him in a way not to be mistaken, was, James felt, not for himself. He looked once more at the Isola Bella. No. He hoped there would not be any more of these. If there were, he must write and stop them.

II

But whether he wanted them or not, more postcards came during the month of his holiday. One from St. Moritz.

Have arrived at our mountain top. It is certainly cool, but also raining. Dripping, bad-tempered walks in the pine woods.

One from Lucerne.

I like this place *much* better. Nice hotel. Nice shops. Sweet little steamers that take us to places with nice restaurants on the lake.

Then one from Lausanne that came on the early autumn morning upon which James was returning to Glasgow.

Arrived here tonight. Am to go to my pension for Young Ladies tomorrow. Awful! Father and Mother remaining here for a week to keep me from feeling *utterly* deserted. Shall write you a letter when I settle down—if ever.

[105]

He had ended up by telling Connie, of course. "These postcards, Mother? They are from Professor Mackinnon Gailes's girl. She cut her hand at the exhibition. I bandaged it."

Connie was impressed. She drew herself up, turned her head on its high neckband, and looked at James like a benevolent stork. "Mackinnon Gailes, dear? Of the university? I didn't know you knew them!"

"I didn't. I just happened to be there."

"But you *must* know them now." How annoying of him merely to shake his head at this when she was eager for more. "Then what about those beautiful postcards from Miss Gailes?"

"I can't stop her from sending them."

"The child must be grateful to you."

Her stepson allowed himself a remote, self-communing smile. "How do you know Miss Gailes is a child, Mother?"

The stork turned its head aside, colored a little and blinked through its eye clips. "Well, dear, isn't she?"

"Been reading the postcards, Mother? Think they seem like a child's?"

The stork's color became deeper. "You should know me better than to ask me a question like that, Bruce."

("Be nice to Connie, James. Even if—well, anyway—be nice to her." He must try to remember that.) "I'm sorry, Mother. No. She's not very old. They've taken her to school in Switzerland."

"They?"

"Professor and Mrs. Gailes."

The stork regained a smiling equanimity and said: "Delightful!" as professors, Switzerland, social importance, life's graces and expensive finishing schools for young ladies rose golden in her mind. Odd that her homespun stepson should touch even the fringe of such things.

But James came to look back with much pleasure on this month spent with Connie and his father. It remained for him a memory of sunshine and friendliness. A ledge on the mountainside where he had flung himself down to rest before he faced round once more and went on climbing.

He had never been on such good terms with his stepmother. A letter had come from Bertha Lyndoch telling her sister of his visit. Of how all was forgiven. Of how glad Walter and she had been to get to know James properly. Of what a promising young man Walter considered James to be, and how they were hoping to see more of him. This was high commendation indeed; for Constance, Bertha and her husband were the final judges in all things. In art, in education, in knowledge of the world.

And for James the long strain of examination had been lifted, leaving him less on edge, less quick, less intolerant perhaps; more self-confident, certainly more mature and thus better able to suffer his stepmother gladly, taking less notice of her uncomfortable ways.

Yet, even though it was to be sunshine and family peace that would remain with him later, there were at the time things less pleasant. The thought of Edith Mackinnon Gailes for one. And there was another. That was their concern for his father, the doctor of Kinaldie. Peter Mennock, James saw, was becoming ever later in starting his rounds of a morning. His faded blue eyes looked heavy now and prematurely old. James saw too that Constance had begun to stop nagging at his father, urging him to be up and out. More than once, indeed, he had caught a look of genuine distress hovering behind the metal eyeglasses.

He was not surprised, therefore, that one morning as he stood smoking his pipe in the front garden and watching the little doctor's figure diminish down the dusty street, the doctor's wife should come to him and tell him of her fears.

"Bruce, I'm worried about your father. Really worried."

James turned to look at her.

"He's never anything but tired now. He's losing all his spring."

"Getting old, Mother."

"Nonsense. Old? No. It's more than that. You must have noticed."

James nodded. But he must take care not to fuss this fussy woman. "Oh, it's nothing, Mother. I'll examine him if you like. Though, of course, he'll never believe I'm a real doctor."

"Oh, Bruce! I wish you would, dear!"

"He hasna got much to do just now or if he has, he doesna say. I daresay I could do what's needed if you took him away for a couple of weeks."

"At once?"

"Yes, at once. Why not?"

Poor Constance stood for a time wrestling with devils. Devils of fruit-picking, of jam-making, of housecleaning, of village ladies who must be visited or received. But her husband won. "Very well. At once, Bruce. If Peter will let me take him." She spoke the last words low and to herself, emotional from the struggle.

"Father will be all right, Mother! And I'll talk to him."

But Constance was retreating back into the house polishing her eye clips.

III

Talking to Peter Mennock proved, however, to be of no use. And Constance had to find her consolation—and no inconsiderable consolation—in the fact that the jam-making and the housecleaning and the visits could take place as she had planned.

The doctor of Kinaldie had his faults. And his son was well aware of them. But now, seeking to persuade him to think of himself, James was at once brought face to face with his father's virtues. Peter Mennock was a good country doctor. He cared about his patients. With that stubbornness which comes sometimes with a sense of waning energy, he argued with his son. A young woman in frail health was expecting a first child. A farmer's wife was dying of a lingering disease. A man, badly injured in the cotton mills, was fighting for his life.

"These folks canna do without me, James. And, anyway, Connie and I have arranged a week or two in the back end."

James did not reply at once. What was it that his father could do for such people that he himself could not? "It's not them I'm thinking about, Father. It's you."

It was his unspoken question that Peter Mennock answered. "Your knowledge is fresh, James. I suppose there's nothing you couldna do for these folk better than I could. Except be me. It's me they want. Me they expect. When they say, 'Send for the doctor!' it's me they see in their minds. And whether you understand that yet or not, it's half a doctor's battle. In Kinaldie, anyway."

But James did understand. He understood too that his father, in his own time and in his own way, was immovable from duty. Thus he was forced to announce his defeat to Constance, repeating once again that there was no cause for alarm.

And so, indeed, it seemed. During the remainder of the young man's stay at home, his father appeared to be better. He was pleased with his son's offer of help at the cost of his own holiday; pleased to have his son drive the pony along dusty farm tracks where the

[108]

berries were already becoming ripe in the tangled hedges and the corn was turning yellow in the hot fields; pleased to drive home again, discussing the case he had just visited, asking his son what he thought and sometimes arguing with him. These were days of happiness and reassurance.

The month that followed was not, strangely, to leave so deep a mark in James's memory. Strangely, since it was in this month the James Mennock whose name would one day be known to surgery was now entering hospital, fresh with high academic honors, eager, single-minded and ready to begin. It was a time of adjustment; of new impressions; a time of settling in. And that, perhaps, was all.

Even the sender of the postcards from Switzerland seemed to have forgotten him; and when James thought of Charlotte and her mother, which was not now uncomfortably often, it was to tell himself that he had too much work to do to bother about silly women and their daughters.

As the days moved into October, however, Charlotte wrote once more. This time a letter.

DEAR DOCTOR MENNOCK,

You must be wondering how your exiled friend is getting on! Father and Mother have been gone for more than three weeks now, so I should have written to you long before this. But the truth is I have been far too *low*. You can imagine how terrible it was saying goodbye to them and knowing that soon they would be in my own dear country while I would be far away and all alone in another!

This is really a very pretty place just outside Lausanne. It is built like a large chalet, and has a terraced garden from which we have a majestic, breath-taking panorama of glorious Lac Leman, which is, of course, the Lake of Geneva. It is still warm enough to have most of our food and do most of our studying out of doors. To begin with, I found it difficult to *think* in the presence of such unutterable beauty. However, I forced myself to recall my vagrant thoughts, and now I am doing really quite well.

It is also still warm enough to bathe in the lake, so three times a week we are marched down by a mistress who stands on the jetty and shows us swimming strokes with one hand—her other hand is holding up her parasol—then marched back again. It is great fun, especially as I am one of the few girls who can swim properly already. I am a junior member of the Western Baths in Hillhead. I don't know if I told you.

Have you read any of Lord Byron's poetry? "The Prisoner of Chillon," for instance? We were taken to visit Chillon yesterday. It is the most romantic castle you ever saw, standing out in the waters of the lake! And—just listen to this—when I got back in the evening, with my head full of it, I found a copy of Lord Byron's poetry without any covers stuffed inside an upside-down flower-pot in a sort of toolshed place in the garden! Very strange, wasn't it? I read it unobserved in a remote spot surrounded by laurels, where the gardener dumps swept-up leaves and things, as we are not allowed to read or even speak anything but French. Heavenly! Lord Byron must have been a really nice man!

The girls and the teachers here are quite pleasant. But you can't possibly be interested, even though they hail from the four corners of the known world. But, oh how I long for the sight of my own kith and kin! Or at least news of them. So write to me at once, please, now that you know my address, and after that as often as you can. Tell me *everything*. I *must* know what you are doing and all about you.

Your sincere friend,
Charlotte Gailes

IV

In the austere privacy of his own hospital bedroom, James read this several times, laughing aloud more than once as he did so. At length, however, he pushed it into a pocket of his white coat and sat thinking.

A ridiculous effusion, of course. And yet its nonsense had set the writer in all her freshness vividly before him. What an odd little creature she was, continuing stubborn and determined in her friend-ship with him. What did she want of him? Looking up, James caught his own reflection in a square piece of mirror hanging on the wall. The tired face of a hard-worked young houseman who had been out of bed most of last night. A large-featured country face crowned with a shock of hair. No. He was no waxwork Adonis upon whom an adolescent girl might pin her romantic dreams. Then why this per-sistence?

And yet he was touched, and in a subtle way flattered, that this young girl, pampered and irresponsible certainly, yet fine-grained, should want his friendship. He drew the letter from his pocket and looked at it thoughtfully once again. "Write to me at once, please, and after that as often as you can." Well? Was he really to enter into a correspondence with this child in every way so unlike himself? With this child whose mother had shown him the door?

James was seldom slow with his decisions. He reached for a pad and pencil. He would scribble out the draft of a letter to Charlotte Gailes now.

DEAR MISS GAILES,

Your letter came today, and I was glad to receive it. I was also glad to see that in spite of some homesickness you are finding Switzerland to your taste; more than you realize, maybe. (Or, no. Was that too heavy-handed? Too adult? Hadn't he better play up? He scored out the last sentence.) . . . receive it. I am truly sorry to read that your spirits are low, because of homesickness, but am all the more honored that, in spite of this, you have troubled to write me a letter. I can only hope that your low spirits will not last much longer, and that things like the scenery and so on will make you forget you are a stranger in a strange land. (As he wrote these words, James smiled. Pleased with himself. What next? Tell her what he was doing? He could tell her the little that would interest her in the fair copy. But these letters she seemed to expect from him? He must get to that. He scratched the mop of hair for a moment with his pencil, then went on.)

It is kind of you to say you want me to write often. I am very sorry to tell you I cannot see my way to do this, Miss Gailes. I will always be your friend and I hope you will be mine. But when I came to your house in July, Professor Mackinnon Gailes and your mother showed me very plainly I was not wanted.

Well, there it is. Even a young lady of your age (no, that wouldn't do. It was patronizing. He scored out the word "age" and substituted "friendliness") must see that I could not possibly undertake to conduct a secret correspondence. It would be against my conscience, and make me feel a cad.

(Again James stopped here and looked at the words he had set down. He sighed. He didn't like them. They seemed, after all, so ponderous, somehow so indelicate, so out of tune with the bright child who was to receive them. And yet she must be told. For a time he sat wondering how he could soften their impact. No. These words must stand. And now, how should he wind up this letter?)

I am, as I say, very sorry to have to write this, and I hope you will not think me hard. Maybe we will meet again sometime when you get back to Glasgow.

Yours very sincerely, (Or "regretfully"? No. That was too high-falutin. "Sincerely" would have to do.)

Without rereading it, he crammed the pad into his pocket with disgust.

But disgust or no disgust, the letter was completed, recopied and sent to Charlotte that same evening. James was not a young man who shirked his duty, merely because he disliked the doing of it.

V

On a wet afternoon some ten days later, the carriage of Professor Mackinnon Gailes stood waiting for the professor's lady by the professor's carriage stone. In the cheerless drip of the sodden afternoon, the horses had became restive and to quiet them the young coachman, a newcomer, had descended from his perch and was standing at their heads.

Presently the front door opened and a timid, meek young woman came out. "She's just comin', Tom," she said, answering the man's handsome, inquiring eyebrows.

"What are *you* dressed up for? Now! Steady, Flora!" The question was addressed to the girl. The admonition, to one of the horses, tossing an impatient head.

"I'm to go wi' her."

"Where to, Jean?"

"The infirmary."

"Infirmary? How's Lizzie?"

"Better. This is the first time she's to get seein' anybody. So *she*"—here the girl nodded towards the house—"said she would come to help me to find where Lizzie is."

"What? Do you mean to tell me ye were frichtit to find yer ain sister at the infirmary?"

Jean nodded and her pale cheeks became pink. But in a moment she found spirit enough to say: "But there's lots o' things I wouldna be frightened for." The good-looking coachman was so newly come that it was not yet known in the kitchen if he were a married man or not. Better to be on the safe side.

Quite automatically, the young man returned the ball. "Is that so? Do ye tell me that now? And what kind of things would they be, I'm wondering?" Following upon which, he further obliged her by looking her up and down with an amused, appraising eye.

"Wheesht! Here she is!"

Edith Gailes had opened the door and was coming down the front steps clutching her waterproof cloak about her long figure with one hand and holding up her umbrella with the other.

Some days ago Lizzie, Edith's cook, had dropped a pot of soup, injuring a foot and scalding a leg so badly that hospital was the only place for her. This morning Jean, also in Edith's employ, having received notice that she might now visit her elder sister, had gone to her mistress to ask what she had better do. The girl, but recently from the country and new to town ways, had shown so much foolish shyness and bewilderment over finding her sister in a great hospital that Edith had, much to the girl's relief, declared she would take her.

Tom jumped to hold the carriage door for his mistress. But before Mrs. Gailes shut her umbrella and got in, she turned to her young parlormaid who was making a move to climb up in front. "Oh, there you are, Jean. Whyever have you been waiting out here in the rain? You really must learn to take care of yourself better! No. Come down from there. Come inside with me. Haven't you got your waterproof cape, Thomas? Under the seat? Well put it on before we start. To the Royal Infirmary, please."

The carriage jogged down University Avenue. On the trees the October leaves hung damp, colorless and sad. Some of them, together with twigs and branches broken off by the violent storms that had ended the quite abnormally fine "exhibition summer," lay prematurely fallen, mixed with the mud of the roadside. Looking towards the park, Edith caught a glimpse of distant outlines—of tawdry domes and stucco magnificence, standing dim, lost and no longer wanted in the Glasgow rain. The bleak disorder left behind after a gigantic and successful carnival. She was glad to be quickly out of sight of it.

Woodlands Road. Charing Cross. Bath Street. Cathedral Street. The Royal Infirmary.

"I hope you've been taking note of how we came," she said to the green girl on the seat opposite. "I expect Cook will want you to be with her whenever you have any free time. I'll try to arrange for you always to get in, whether it's a visiting period or not. Do you know this part of Glasgow? Or have you never been up here before?"

To which Jean answered, "Yes, Mum." And they both got out.

VI

At the office a cheerful young porter was helpful. He found the name of the patient for the important-seeming lady, then volunteered to take her up. Edith and her maid followed him through the labyrinth of the great hospital. Stairs. Passages. Glimpses of wards, of high white beds, of starched nurses working, hovering.

Again Edith admonished the timid girl who followed to take note of how they went.

"Here you are," their guide said at length. "Oh, there's the Ward Sister. You'll find you own way out, Mum, won't you?"

Mrs. Mackinnon Gailes gave him a half-crown and thanked him, then set off with the Sister down the long ward, chatting suitably as she went and looking with a detached interest at each bed and its contents as she passed them by, much in the same way as she would have chatted and looked at each clump of blooms in a country friend's herbaceous border.

And yet to put it thus is to do her some injustice. No one, who was not a close intimate, would have known she was a shy person, with a shy person's self-enforced poise and a shy person's arrogance. She had much disliked the thought of this hospital visit. Yet from a sense of responsibility to her servants she had made herself come.

"Oh, Cook! There you are! See who I've brought to visit you! Jean, untie the parcel of things we packed for Cook." She turned now to look at the young woman who had come with her and was surprised to find that the girl's face was flushed and that tears stood in her eyes.

Edith could understand timidity very well. The great building, this great machine of healing with its wards and its corridors, its impersonality and its awesome self-assurance, was altogether too much for this country child who as yet knew so little of the city. She put her hand on her arm. "Go over and speak, my dear, while I ask Sister how Cook is." She turned to the Sister with a smile and an apologetic lift of her eyebrows. "A little excited, perhaps. And what about our patient, Sister?"

The Sister turned with her to move up the ward a little. "Much better, Mrs. Mackinnon Gailes. But here's the house surgeon. He saw me dressing the burn this morning. You can ask him."

It would be difficult to say which of the two would have been most thankful to be allowed to turn and run—the tall woman or the red-haired young man in the white coat. But flight was impossible for either.

Edith had faced many situations, but none just like this one. And now she was quite at a loss. She could think of no set pattern, no rule that would fit it. Seeing it as her duty, she had severely snubbed this young man for the freedom he had dared to take with her daughter. And yet since then Charlotte, foolish in her innocence, had, Edith knew, been sending him picture postcards while they traveled. She had of course protested, but the child had driven her so hard with question and argument that Edith, fearing to give this ridiculous friendship too much importance either by flat prohibition or too adult explanation, had ended by letting the postcards go, comforting herself with the thought that Charlotte must very soon forget him.

But now this. And there was no time to think about it. Thus it was something very like panic that dictated Edith's behavior.

"Doctor, Mrs. Mackinnon Gailes has come to see this patient." Here the Sister nodded towards the bed where Lizzie and Jean were now deep in talk. "Mrs. Mackinnon Gailes, this is Doctor Mennock."

James looked into the eyes of Charlotte's mother, but these eyes betrayed no sign of recognition. So that was how it was to be? Then no recognition would appear in his own. A stiff how-do-you-do; a stiff bow. But neither held out a hand though color rose in the face of each.

As she stood watching, the Ward Sister wondered. Why should this rather self-important woman, who had bothered to show herself so much well-bred politeness, suddenly become rigid? Why should the young doctor, who was not ungenial and certainly did not bother to give himself airs, now be speaking with an icy precision she had so far never heard him use? Why, when his report was quickly given, should he swing abruptly on his heel and walk from the ward?

VII

It was while this new hurt still tingled that James received his second letter from Charlotte. Two days later it came, while his anger still smoldered hot at the thought of Charlotte's mother. Why it should smolder so hotly it would have been difficult for him to say. A silly woman had refused to know him. That was all. He was not, surely, in love with this woman's school-girl daughter, a young girl he had only seen twice in his life? And yet already there was little doubt that, in everything relating to Charlotte, the young James had at this time developed quick sensibilities, a strangely quick capacity for taking hurt.

Off duty and getting back late, he found the letter propped on the mantelpiece of his sitting room. What did this mean? This handwriting? This Swiss stamp? Hadn't he told Charlotte Gailes he did not want to go on corresponding? He tore open the envelope, frowning.

DEAR DOCTOR MENNOCK,

Of course I mean to go on writing to you! Why shouldn't I go on writing to my friends? No, you are not a cad and you are not a monster. I think you are a very nice man. And I told my parents so every time your name was mentioned. I also told them I should go on writing to you, unless they could prove to me that you were a *low type*, which, of course, they can't. So let me hear no more about bad consciences and secret correspondence.

I won't be home for Christmas so you won't get a glimpse of me. My parents are coming out again and we are going to Zürich to spend it with a Swiss professor who was a bosom friend, or something, of my father when he was studying in Heidelberg a hundred years ago. He has a very large family, I hear. Which may be nice, or may not. But it should be great fun to see a real Swiss Christmas. They make a mighty fuss about it, I am told. But I shall miss home too.

My polishing and finishing, whatever that means, goes on. Though I don't feel at all polished or finished yet! Still I daresay I shall be glittering like the furniture when next you see me. They say my French is a little better anyway, and my piano-playing too. They should be. I like French and music and I am working at them quite hard.

Now, please! No more nonsense!

Your sincere friend,
CHARLOTTE GAILES

James read and reread this. His face had changed. The frown

had gone and he stood with his back to the fire, his shoulders against the mantelpiece, his hands in his pockets, staring before him, amused and smiling. The young girl in the white summer dress whose image stayed so persistently with him, had given him back something her mother had, it seemed, tried to take from him. He nodded to himself slowly. Yes. Charlotte was right. He was not a cad and he was not a monster.

For a time he lingered thinking. Then he flung down the letter on his table and set himself a chair. The stark unkindness of her mother's treatment of him had, he now decided, given him permission to write to Charlotte whenever he felt like it. He adjusted the lamp, drew paper and ink towards him, put back a strand of hair and took up his pen.

CHAPTER ELEVEN

I

The firelight moved and flickered on the walls of Sir James's bedroom. The reading lamp by his bedside was lit but the old man was not reading. He lay propped against his pillows, his book put to one side, his long hands straight and crossed, one over the other, before him. He lay motionless staring into vacancy, looking into his memory, unaware of the still world around him. The chimes from the university announcing that the old year had only another quarter of an hour of life were indeed the last sounds that had reached his consciousness.

"Grandfather, are you all right?"

It took him a moment to come back; to realize that the door had been opened without noise; that his granddaughter was standing there looking down upon him. The girl looked pale in the lamplight and there were loose strands of copper hair. He guessed she had been working. "Hullo, Maggs. Of course I'm all right. Why?"

"You were lying so still. Not even blinking."

"Thinking my thoughts. That's all. What have you been doing?"

"Finishing another chapter. I'll have something to show you tomorrow."

"What way not tonight?"

"Because you might get interested and forget to go to sleep."

Sir James's face clouded. He was not used to being managed like this. But his reason cleared it again almost at once. "Well, well. Mebbe you're right. I'll have pleasure in telling you how bad it is tomorrow. Listen, Maggs! The New Year! Open the window. It's a fine night. I want to hear the horns. What about your Granny?"

"I've just looked in. She's asleep."

"Better leave her."

"That's what I thought." As she crossed to the window and threw it up, a breeze from the south invaded the bedroom, filling it with a caressing freshness and fluttering the curtains. Now Margaret stood with her back to him, her hands still holding the upflung window sash looking out into the glowing night, listening.

The twelve strokes sounded ponderously one after the other. And then, in a moment, the horns of a hundred ships, high-pitched or deep, came to them from the distant harbor. Factory horns from still further off joined in. Glasgow had raised a voice that was oddly harmonious to greet the New Year.

But at last, after some minutes, when the strange music had dwindled down to silence, she closed the window and turned round. Her grandfather was holding out an affectionate hand. "A Happy New Year, Maggs."

As she bent to kiss his brow he saw that her eyes were shining. What had touched her, he wondered? Was it merely that she was still at times abnormally on edge, still brittle? But whatever it was, he found no sense in encouraging emotion. He released her hand. "There's a decanter of port," he said. "I told them to bring it up. We'll drink to the New Year."

"Expecting someone?" she asked as she turned to get it.

"Expecting you." She had, he saw, regained her calmness as she came back to his bedside with two part-filled glasses to toast the newly begun year. "Fill up your glass again," he said when that ceremony was over. "Don't run away at once. Stay and talk to me."

She sat down in his chair by the fireside, bent forward to fling on some pieces of coal, then lay back waiting for him to speak.

"You look as if you had been working hard, Maggs."

"Yes, I was." But he would have to see what she had written before they could talk about it.

Now for a time he lay watching her with an old man's affection, as she rested, relaxed and untidy, golden and fragile there in the firelight, nibbling at a biscuit and sipping her wine.

Presently she asked: "You were far away when I came in just now, darling. What were you thinking about?"

"About your father."

"My father!"

"Yes. And what way should I not think about your father? What's queer about that?" Why had she become so tense? Why she was sitting up now?

"Oh, no reason. No reason and every reason, I suppose. I've wanted to talk about him for a long time."

"Well? And what way did you not talk then?"

"I was afraid it might upset you."

"Upset me, Maggs?"

"Yes."

He did not ask why. He lay back considering. What did she know? What had she found out? Had he been unwise to let her loose among his papers? But after all, he had argued, she was an adult woman now, with adult strength to meet the tragedy and comedy of things. More emotionally adult, he had judged, than most women; certainly more than Charlotte.

"What kind of young man was my father, Grandfather?"

He did not speak quite at once, giving himself time. "Your Granny and I loved him dearly, Maggs," he said at length.

She set down her glass and turned, grasping one arm of her chair with both hands and addressing him earnestly. "Of course! But, Grandfather, was my father not all—did he sometimes make you both unhappy?"

Again he was slow to speak, and then in his turn he asked her a question. "What have you read about your father? I didna think you had got as far as that yet."

"Not systematically. Only by chance. I haven't found out anything really. Only— But why?"

"I should have thought more about this, Maggs. You've been through a lot yourself. Your nerves—well, anyway, I see I should have kept your father's story under lock and key."

"But I *should* have heard about him! Yes, and about my mother too, long ago!"

"Calm yourself, lassie! Who said you should have heard about them long ago? That was for me to say. And, forbye, when have you ever asked about them before? Here, Maggs, come here to me." His hand went out to catch her own as she came to him. "It was all a sore business, very sore! But I daresay you're right. When you turned a woman you should have been told about your parents—or the most of it anyway. But now, as I am, don't ask me. When you and I are better fit to talk about it then I'll mebbe tell you."

"I'm sorry, Grandfather. I'm being excitable and ridiculous."

"Never heed about that. But I want you to promise something."

"Yes?"

"I want you to promise not to try to find out from the diaries before I can explain to you myself."

"Why, darling?"

"I sent you to Woodside Terrace because I thought it would divert you and occupy your mind."

"You know it has."

"Well then, leave it at that. Go on with your grandmother and me and leave your father and mother. Is that a bargain?" He released her hand as she nodded assent. "And say nothing to your Granny. There. Go back to your chair."

The room fell back into silence. Fresh flames sprang up and flickered. The girl sat staring at them as she sipped her wine. Sir James lay watching her, wondering what was passing in her mind.

II

"What do you think of Joe Struan?" he asked presently.

She came up out of her thoughts and turned towards him. "The paragon?"

"The paragon, as you call him."

"I quite like him now."

"Now?"

"I didn't at first. Why are you asking?"

"You've been working with him. I wanted your opinion." She seemed on the defensive somehow. What did that signify? "I had a letter from Canada the other day," Sir James went on. "From a man who was one of my students, oh, twenty-five years since. Made his life on the other side of the water. Done well as a surgeon. And turned professor like myself. Now he's asking if I have a young man —a disciple, he calls him—to put forward for a Canadian professorship. I was thinking about Joe."

"Well? Why not, Grandfather? But can anyone so shy lecture?"

"Of course! And anyway it's what he says that counts."

"And the work he's doing for you?"

"That won't take much longer."

"Just the man then, I should say." Showing apparently no further interest in the paragon and his transatlantic prospects, Margaret got up, set down her glass, bade her grandfather good night and left him to ruminate.

As a great artist may have an art child, a pupil of brilliance, quicker than others to absorb and profit by his tenets, so in another sphere did the large and strange young man who was Joseph Struan stand in his relationship to Sir James Mennock.

Yes, a queer boy, the old man reflected. But clever. A boy that would not fit in everywhere maybe. But a boy that should be given his chance. It was true he had a shy, uncertain way with him. Yes. It was a pity. His extreme shyness was certainly against him. Perhaps it had its roots in the young man's background, in his plain beginnings. Now suppose Joe had the university background such as he, James Mennock, had stepped into when he married the daughter of old Professor Gailes, suppose Joe had been his own son? Or suppose, Sandy—?

But now, with a poignant wrench, the old man's thoughts were caught and thrust into another channel. Sandy. The raptures and sorrows their only son had brought to Charlotte and himself. Only he, his father, knew the whole of Sandy's story. Charlotte had never quite known the end. Chance had put it into his power to shield her from it. And he had done so.

And Margaret? Tonight Sandy's daughter had seemed so oddly roused, so nervously curious about her father. Why hadn't he realized that in handing over his keys, he was handing to a girl already made sensitive by loss the keys of yet another tragedy that concerned her.

Sir James sat forward. His beating pulse, the red spots on each cheek, and his wide-awake distress would not have pleased his doctors. What had made him, he now asked himself passionately, keep these ridiculous telltale diaries? Why through the years that fixed compulsion, that freak pleasure in setting down his days? Even to his poor boy's end.

No. It would be much better if Sandy's daughter never knew. She had promised to leave her father and his story for the present. But to extract that promise he had had to say he would tell her later. Yet need he ever tell her quite all? Need she know any more than he had told her grandmother? He did not think so. But then there were the diaries. That diary for 1930, the year of Sandy's death. In which, of course, he had noted everything. Sooner or later it must come to be opened by his granddaughter. Was there nothing he could do to stop it? Was there no way of taking it from its box without her knowledge? There must be if he would only stop to think? This could not be too difficult to contrive. Now if he—

Yes. That would be workable. It was quite simple really. And the sooner the better.

"Good New Year to you, Joe! Come in, come in."

It was the second of January.

The paragon was standing, dazed and enormous, in the doorway of Sir James's study peering mistily through his lenses. As he came forward he realized that the old man sitting by the fireside was extending a hand in greeting. "Happy New Year, sir. Sorry I—I can't shake hands." He spoke self-consciously, anticipating Sir James's disapproval. His right hand and wrist were stiffly bandaged.

"What's this? Been out on the hills?"

"I—I was climbing in Glencoe yesterday."

Sir James shook his head in mock disgust at the uncomfortable creature standing there on the hearthrug before him. Climbing and walking were, he knew, the only means of getting rid of some of the inexhaustible vigor which this young giant's eyes would allow to him. "That's one way of spending New Year's Day. What have you done to your hand?"

"I—I've only sprained it. I've been to hospital. They photographed it. There's nothing broken."

"You should learn to look after your hands in your line of business."

"Yes, sir."

"Sit down, Joe." Sir James watched him lower his large and today somewhat stiff person into the chair opposite his own. "I want you to do something for me." Then, as the paragon seemed to find nothing to say to this, he fired a question at him. "By the way, how do you like my granddaughter, Joe?"

"She's— Mrs. Raymond's very nice, sir."

It was so usual for the young man to show confusion and embarrassment that it did not occur to Sir James to deduce anything from these now. "Has she ever told you what she's doing across there at Woodside Terrace?"

"Yes. Looking through your papers."

"Well, that's part of it anyway. Has she ever shown you anything?"

"She—she once showed me a snapshot of her father that she had come across."

"I didna know she had found one. What way did she not show it to me?"

"I don't know, sir." The paragon was troubled. Had he done Mrs. Raymond a disservice of some kind? Didn't she, for some reason, want her grandfather to know that this photograph of his own son existed. He looked across at the old man apprehensively. But Sir James now seemed to be disposed to let the question of the photograph go. He was sitting with his hands before him, the tips of the long fingers placed one against the other, deep seemingly, in reflection. The young man waited.

"It was about her father I wanted to speak to you, Joe," Sir James said at length. "You'll have heard tell about my son, Alexander, I daresay?"

"Yes, sir."

"What have you heard?"

Confusion returned to the paragon's features. "I haven't heard very much, Sir James."

"It's mebbe just as well that you havena," the old man said, leaning forward and directing his eyes ruefully towards the fire as though, almost, to avoid meeting the eyes of his visitor. "My son's short story wasna very much to his credit. Nor to mine, I doubt. It's an old story but even now—I didna do right by him, Joe."

"I'm—I'm—sure you did everything that was right," the paragon ventured, feeling at once the banality of his words as he said them.

"No. I didna do right. And the lassie he married was—well— Of course we did what we could for the both of them. But it was Sandy that was hopeless. He was weak. Weak and plausible to the end." Sir James stopped, then added: "And lovable."

Joe Struan felt deeply sorry. Why had Alexander Mennock's father brought him here and given himself the pain of saying these things? Especially since he had never spoken of his son before. But the old man was about to give him the answer.

"I'm the only one that knows the end of his story. Even my wife doesna know the real way of it. I was fool enough to put it in my diary. I've always had the diary habit. And it's there for my son's daughter to read. I've been thinking it would be better for her not to see it."

"But are you sure she hasn't seen it, Sir James? She's very interested in her father. She's been asking even me questions."

The old man started. "*You* questions? No. She would have told me if she had. Joe, I want you to find the diary for the year 1930 and take it out of the box without Margaret knowing you've been there."

"But she has the keys, sir."

"No she hasna." James smiled wanly as he drew them from his pocket. "I took them out of her bag. She thinks she has lost them. She'll have the good luck to find them again when you've brought that diary here to me. Will you do that for me? Will you manage to do it this morning? Even with your left hand? Margaret will not be there and Miss McQueen has a holiday."

The paragon put the keys into his pocket and stood up. "I—I would do anything, anything at all," he said, "to spare Mrs. Raymond's feelings!"

As the old man turned to look at him, surprised by this fervor, Margaret came in.

"I'm sorry, Grandfather, I thought you were—"

"Come in, Maggs. You can see who it is."

"Doctor Struan! Happy New Year!"

Sir James' eyes traveled back and forth between the two.

"Whatever have you done to your hand?" his granddaughter was asking. "Glencoe, I expect? But not serious? Never mind. I'll shake your left!"

They seemed to have reached an easy friendship, this girl and this large young man, who now stood before her displaying a mouthful of strong teeth in a large grin. So that was it? There could be little doubt about the boy's feelings. But what about his granddaughter? Sir James watched her as she followed Struan from the room, then sat listening to the sound of their voices as they lingered talking by the open front door; to the clear voice of his granddaughter and to the resonant, stammering replies, accompanied here and there by low-pitched, explosive chuckles.

It had not before occurred to him to wonder how these two stood, one with the other. They had, it seemed, much to talk about.

Margaret's last chapters lay here beside him. Once again she had found his early manhood for him, bringing it back, distilling it out in her narrative. Might the story now repeat itself? Had a gifted, gauche young doctor, who had thus far fought for all his privileges, become attached to a handsome young woman who had known privilege as a birthright? It might be. But here the parallel ended. These other two were older. Different, in a different world. And Margaret had none of the absurd enchantment of the child who had become her grandmother.

Sir James thought of these first encounters with Charlotte's parents as Margaret had brought them back to him. Of his anger and his bitterness. Yet how confident, how persistent he had been! Was it the mulish persistence of a country lout? At all events, he had doggedly returned to the attack and had indeed resorted at last to the strong tactics of desperation. He could not picture Struan daring to do what he had done. But he would not need to. Neither himself nor Charlotte would ever try to intervene like the old professor and his wife.

But here was Charlotte herself. "Really!" she was exclaiming. "What on earth can Margaret be finding to say to that Doctor Struan of yours, James? She's been standing with him there for hours! And it's bitter! She's probably catching pneumonia and everything else! I wish she would come back in and shut the door!"

CHAPTER TWELVE

I

It was a wet, cold evening in late October. An evening for depression and low spirits, Walter Lyndoch felt. And since depression and low spirits were things that he detested, he decided on his way home from work to pay a visit to the Glasgow Art Club in the hope of finding ten minutes' congenial talk and in the certainty of having a glass of sherry before the clubroom fire.

Walter was delighted with his visit. For there he picked up a piece of news that would, he was certain, give great pleasure to his wife Bertha. Warmed and stimulated, he left the club and continued his journey homeward. Now, in the lighted tramcar, his large body swayed back and forth upon its seat, inflated with complacency.

At the stop after Botanic Gardens he descended carefully, keeping the tramcar waiting. No jumping off while it was moving! He had long since renounced the heedless agility that goes with youth and slenderness. A nasty evening. But in a step or two he would be home. He turned up the collar of his overcoat and set off, comforting himself with the thought of the news he would presently give his wife, news that a certain famous woman pianist had been engaged to come to Glasgow next winter to play with the Scottish Orchestra. This lady was German and had been a fellow student with Bertha in Dresden. She had since those days climbed to the top of her profession.

Walter Lyndoch was one of those who are flattered by the notice of prominent artists but neither know, nor yet appear to want to know, anything of the art they practice. A liking, it may be, for reflected glory. At all events, nothing pleased him better than to have one such within his too hospitable clutches. And here was a celebrity who must inevitably fall straight into them, whom Bertha must certainly invite to stay. Even now, shrinking within his upturned coat collar in the rain and darkness, his enthusiasm could already hear the grand piano in Bertha's music room thunder and tremble while celebrity exercised its fingers. "Staying with us? Of course she was staying with us! Devoted to my wife! Girls together! *She* took up *her* music professionally. But if Bertha had done the same, everybody says—"

And, indeed, the celebrity appeared never to have forgotten that Bertha was her friend. Her Christmas cards—her secretary kept a permanent list—came regularly from different parts of the world.

Now, a little breathless, Walter stood before his own front door, while his fat rain-wet fingers searched his pockets for his bunch of keys. Yes. It was great news. He would have a happy evening talking this visit over, consulting with Bertha, discussing what they must do. Already, indeed, fantasy was beginning to run away with good sense. A semicivic reception? This celebrity had a very big name. Or perhaps not even semi, if the Lord Provost were not too busy. But a fuss, at any rate. Lots of fuss. He chose his latch key, shook it clear of the others and thrust it into the lock.

But before he could turn it, the door was pulled open from the inside. "Walter! I heard your key! How are you? What a horrible night!"

Walter had seldom wanted to see his sister-in-law less but good nature would not, of course, allow him to show it. "Hello, Connie. Where have you come from? Haven't seen you for a long time." He shut out the night behind him and extended a damp hand.

She shook it demurely and not without respect. She liked her brother-in-law much better than he liked her. In the eyes of Constance, Bertha's husband could do no wrong. "Oh, I am very well, thank you, Walter," she said. "I've come from Kinaldie, of course. I felt I must run up to talk to Bertha. She has kept me overnight. She thinks I ought to talk to you too."

"Nothing serious, I hope?"

"Well—" Constance raised her eyes to the ceiling, then sighed and shrugged. "Oh, you'll hear all about it later. I mustn't keep you standing in a wet overcoat. Go and take it off."

Walter went to do so, frowning. Thank goodness that poor soul, Peter Mennock, had descended from the skies and taken Constance to his bosom and Kinaldie. Walter had often wondered how Peter liked having her in both these places, then had as often reminded himself with relief that it was none of his business. But was there ever such a woman for dropping the temperature? For puncturing the balloons of cheerfulness? Why did she have to come just tonight? And what news could she have to tell in any way comparable to his own?

Some moments later, he was bending to soap his hands in his dressing room washbasin when he heard his wife's voice behind him. "Walter, Connie's here."

"I know, I know." As he turned to her, Bertha saw that the large fat child who was her husband looked displeased. "I'm sorry," she said and bent to kiss the sulky face that was on the point of receiving a covering of soapsuds.

He straightened himself. "Bertha, I've great news for you. Guess who's coming to play with the Scottish Orchestra next winter? And she'll be in Glasgow for several days at least."

"Who?"

He gave the celebrity's name and quoted authority.

"That should be interesting."

He looked at her with surprise. "Is that all you have to say?"

"Well? What else would you like me to say?"

"But she's your friend! She must stay here!"

"Here!"

This German virtuoso had grown larger than life, Bertha reflected. She had sprouted since student days, the crashing personality of a prime minister. "Have her here, Walter? I scarcely think—"

"Of course."

But Bertha was worried this evening. She could find no patience for this nonsense. "Hurry up, dear," she said. "Don't keep dinner waiting."

"But do you mean to say she can't—?"

"No, Walter. Only over my dead body!"

Walter turned back to his washbasin and began to soap his plump, unhappy face.

II

But in the winter that followed it was to this generous, rather simple man and his wife that young James Mennock was continually to turn. And it was the anxiety of this same evening which was to draw him to them.

A telephone call from Walter found James in hospital and brought him across to hear what his stepmother had to say. She was distressed about his father. Peter and she had taken the holiday arranged for the late autumn but Peter seemed to have received little good from it. And what now did her son and the others think he ought to do? Or rather be made to do, since her husband was being stubborn and unreasonable.

In James's later memory this was a time of dragging anxiety; of taking, for the first time perhaps, adult responsibility; of learning to overrule his father's hitherto stronger will. James had gone to Kinaldie to persuade him to see a specialist. But the little man, knowing more, it may be, than he cared to admit, had refused to see one.

Through the weeks of November James had by letter and in person fought with him; using all the arguments, reasonable and emotional, that are used at such times. His father's unkindness to those who loved and depended upon him. His foolishness in refusing to see someone who could almost certainly put him right. His father's selfishness to himself, James, by keeping him on tenterhooks when he should have his mind free to learn all he could at the Infirmary. Such arguments. In the end the growing force of James's character won.

Early in December Peter Mennock at last gave way and allowed his son to arrange a vist to a specialist. It was a day that was to remain with James in all its detail. Connie and her anxiety could not, of course, be kept at home. Nor could she be kept from the specialist's waiting room during the examination of her husband. James was obliged to sit with her while her nervousness chattered unceasingly. Thank goodness Bruce had managed at last to arrange this! What did Bruce think the specialist would say? Dear me! Here was a picture of King Edward driving in a motor car in the *Illustrated London News!* She was sure motor cars were dangerous. Didn't Bruce think it was a little too daring of the King, considering his great responsibilities? What a time they were taking! But Bruce's idea that they should go straight home, whatever the verdict, was much the best. Much less harassing for his father. It was nice of the Lyndochs wanting them for the night, but Bruce would find time later on and run out west and tell them the news, wouldn't he? Bruce promised.

His father emerged from the consulting room with a favorable verdict—for the benefit of Constance, James saw. Now the great man was at his front door bidding them all goodbye.

"Nothing to worry about, Mrs. Mennock, nothing at all. Goodbye, Doctor, and see that Mrs. Mennock looks after you! Keep her up to scratch! And remember to look after yourself! *You* know Doctor Peter Mennock better than I do, so treat him with respect. And pet him, spoil him for a month or two. Goodbye! Goodbye!"

The kind of speech made on many a consultant's doorstep. But as they descended to the street he called to James: "I'll be up at the Royal tomorrow. I'll see you, Mennock. Or you can ring me tonight if you like."

"I'll ring you tonight, sir."

"He wanted to tell you the truth," his father said, referring to this at the door of their railway carriage as James saw them off. His stepmother was out of earshot.

"What truth, Father? Did he say more to you than I've heard?"

"Not much. He spoke about *you* most of the time."

"Me?"

"He says they're talking about you. He thinks you have a future. I feel it would mebbe be a good thing now if—"

The whistle had blown here. His father had climbed in, then turned to lean from the open window.

"If what, Father? What were you going to say?"

"Oh, I canna mind. I was pleased with what he said about you, anyway. I'll keep going as long as I can, James."

The Ayrshire train began to move out into the darkness. Each waved to the other, then James turned back down the platform, his question left unanswered, his heart heavy.

From the railway station he had taken himself to the Lyndochs, not only because Constance had asked him to see them but because they shared his anxieties and were now his good friends.

It was from there, later in the evening, that he telephoned and was told what he had already more than half expected. His father would go on for some time still. Months. This winter, it might be. Even longer. The specialist could not tell.

"And then, sir?"

"We'll hope he'll go straight out, Mennock. I wish I had better news for you than this."

James had spoken from the Lyndoch's sitting room. They did not ask for details. They knew from his voice.

"Is the whisky on the sideboard, Bertha?" Walter said. "Jimmie and I are going to drink some whisky. No, Jimmie, I know whisky's not one of your drinks, but it's going to be tonight."

It had helped to be with the Lyndochs. To talk now, of the future, of himself, of Constance. What he had better do.

It had too—strangely, James sometimes thought later—helped, when he got back to hospital on that bleak night, to find a letter from a schoolgirl in Switzerland telling him of the madcap elopement of some girl in her school. A happening that could, in itself, rouse no interest in him. But the letter once again brought the picture of its writer before him. A bright picture in which James found consolation.

III

Indeed, looking back over the drab texture of that winter, Charlotte's letters seemed to run through it like a thread of silver. Wilful, high-spirited, sometimes merely ridiculous. But always the letters of a young girl who was delicately sensitive.

Yet James, maturing quickly now as trouble and responsibility pressed about him, would have been strange indeed had not this child's writing to him caused him some uneasiness and doubt. Had he been in any kind of relationship with her parents he would have gone to them, spoken of her and asked them what he must do. But the door of Professor Mackinnon Gailes was closed against him. And hurt pride forbade James to try again to force it open.

He had at last confided in Bertha Lyndoch, even showing her some of Charlotte's outpourings.

"Do you want her to stop writing, James?" Bertha looked up smiling from a letter she had been reading.

"No. It's about all the fun I do get these days."

"But you think her parents don't know?"

"She says she's told them. But I don't think they can know she's writing a letter every week. Sometimes oftener."

"Well? What am I to say? If you like answering them—"

He smiled. "It's something to do."

Bertha had sat considering while the fire flickered on the walls of her softly lit music room; and her husband lay back in his chair emitting thick, contented puffs of smoke from his pipe and watching the light tremble and move among the broken colors of his monster Hornel.

What, Bertha wondered, was going on in that boy's head? Behind those too earnest, strained young features? He kept replying to these letters. What were his reasons? Amusement? Loneliness? Feelings he had not defined, even to himself. "What do *you* think about this, Walter?"

Walter Lyndoch removed his eyes from the possession he was never done admiring, twisted round his large, plump body in his deep chair, looked first at his wife and then at his guest. "Let the correspondence go on, Jimmie. Who's it doing any harm to, anyway?"

"James doesn't want her to do anything that might get her into trouble later."

"Rubbish! Jimmie's suffering from too much conscience, if that's what he thinks. What's wrong with this lassie writing him letters, if she's glad to write them and he's glad to get them?"

It was not so simple as that. Still, knowing the burden James carried, knowing the story of James's hospital encounter with Charlotte's mother and being James's warm partisan, Bertha allowed herself to decide that her husband was right.

So the letters continued to go between these two young people, forging bonds that neither perhaps quite took note of. Nonsense. Self-confession. Self-revelation. Then as the months went by, James found Charlotte's tone begin to deepen. She was growing up.

> You may think I am being idiotic, but sometimes I lie in bed at night wondering what you are doing. A hospital must be a very frightening place, sometimes. Do you mind that? I don't think I could bear it. No. Perhaps I could force myself to bear it, if I had to. I wonder? I am a fearful coward.

Again:

> We were out walking early yesterday morning and got so hungry that we went into the station to buy coffee and hot sausages from the platform wagon. They are always to be had when the Simplon night express is expected. Its arrival is always great fun to watch anyway. As we stood munching, it came in, and we saw a group of skinny little children being helped out of it, then stand about waiting for someone to fetch them. I asked the nursish-looking person in charge of them who they were. She said they were consumptive slum children from Paris who were being given two months in the mountains at the expense of some kind person. I am sure two months isn't nearly enough. I made everybody deliver up

their pocket-money (bad grammar) which was enough to buy the children coffee and sausages too. Some of them seemed too tired or bewildered or something to take much interest. Now I can't get their pinched little faces out of my head. Awful, isn't it?

And again:

Do you know, Doctor James, you haven't said a word about your father for a long time. Why don't you? How is he? You may say this is nonsense, but I feel I am getting to know you so well from your letters, that I am beginning to be able to read between your lines! Months ago you told me the consultant in Glasgow had said he would be able to go on working. Surely your father was all right, if he said that? Yet there are times when your letters are—what can I say?—too sprightly or too solemn or something. Of course I don't mind that. But what I mean is, you seem to be using words to hide behind, not to tell me what you are thinking. Or am I writing rubbish? More rubbish than usual, that is? But tell me all about him. I hate not knowing.

By the end of February, James had completed his six months' span as a house surgeon and, since his father continued on his feet and would not hear of his coming to Kinaldie, James was able to make arrangements for a further six. Though the future Sir James Mennock's gifts as a surgeon could not, in these first six months, help beginning to proclaim themselves—his flair, his cool intelligence, those astonishing hands—the young James, forcing himself to turn his back upon ambition and seeing at this time nothing but the life of a country doctor before him, judged it wise to continue for a like period as a medical houseman.

He was able to do this for three months. Then, in the beginning of June, Walter Lyndoch arrived one afternoon to tell James there had been a wire from Kinaldie. Peter Mennock had died suddenly. And rather than wire to the hospital direct, there was a request that he, Walter, should break the news. Bertha and he were, even now, on their way to Constance who hoped they would bring her stepson with them.

A few dazed arrangements and James went. He had expected this for months. And yet its coming left him foolishly bewildered.

But not for long. Bewilderment, as James quickly came to see, was not a state that could accomplish much. There were mishaps in the cotton mills. Wounds had to be bound up. Babies chose to be born. Working folks came to the door of Gowan Bank, apologetic and shiftless, asking what they must do. James had to turn to. Even in the three days that elapsed before Peter Mennock was laid beside James's mother in Kinaldie churchyard, James had begun to work.

When the funeral was over, Walter and Bertha Lyndoch stayed a day longer, then went, leaving Constance, as was decided in family conclave, to look after the house of her already much occupied stepson.

And, by the time the end of June was coming into sight, this oddly assorted couple had settled down to their new routine. In the village the young doctor became popular immediately. Was he not one of themselves? A boy grown up among them? And was he not the old doctor's son? Besides he seemed to be trying so hard, seemed so anxious to do his best. Then, presently the village began to find that James was clever. Here and there it began to be said that Peter Mennock's son, however unlike his spruce little father, however unkempt his hair, however negligent his clothes, showed skill much above the skill of Peter Mennock.

James was sorry for Constance. He was much too busy, too little at home to be annoyed by her ways. Pale, but in appearance much the same as usual, she moved about the house in the dignity of unrelieved black, polishing and arranging even more than usual. Brass shone even more brightly. Floors received even more wax. Peggy and Davie received even more instructions.

"It looks to me as if you were overdoing it, Mother," he said to her one day.

"Overdoing it, Bruce?"

"You never seem to me to stop working. Why do you not go up to Aunt Bertha's for a day or two?"

"It's very good of you, Bruce dear, but what would you do?"

"The house wouldn't run away. There's Peggy."

"I could never leave this house to an inexperienced girl like Peggy!" She stopped for a moment, then asked: "Or perhaps you don't want me here. Perhaps I'm—"

"Of course I want you, Mother! And everything's fine! Forget what

I said!" James had found himself almost shouting. For there were tears in her eyes and her handkerchief was in her hand. "Well, I must go and get on." And so he escaped, not having acquired, yet, the equipment to deal with this kind of feminine response.

And Charlotte? Even in these days of sorrow and preoccupation James found his thoughts turning towards her. Not so much, perhaps, towards the writer from Switzerland, but rather towards the half-child, half-woman with whom he had spent his graduation day.

He had written a few words telling her of his father's death. But she did not seem to have received them. More than one letter came; the last from Paris, telling him that her mother had arrived in Lausanne to fetch her and that she would soon be home. She did not mention his loss, nor, oddly enough, did she mention an early meeting. Difficulties had not, it seemed, occurred to her. To James these difficulties *had* occurred. But why should he meet her? And when would there be time? With every argument of common sense, he thrust the thought of seeing her from him.

And yet the meeting came. And sooner than either of them expected.

V

In the first days of July, his father's affairs made it necessary for James to visit Glasgow. He would take an early train, he decided, do what he had to do in the first half of the day and get back in time to see some, at least, of his sick in the second half.

St. Enoch's Station, when James arrived there, was busy. Long distance travelers, luggage and porters were streaming from another platform. The night train had, it seemed, just come in from London. James turned to the bookstall to buy a morning newspaper. People were crowding round it. Taking advantage of his height, he pitched down his money over the shoulders of others, caught the salesman's eye and stretched out a long arm. As he did so, he felt a firm grasp upon the other. He struggled from among the crowd and turned round.

"Doctor James!"

"Miss Gailes!"

It was Charlotte and yet not Charlotte. In the year he had not seen her she had become taller, he thought, thinner certainly, and her maturing features had become more delicate. Her deepening

[136]

color told him that now she was conscious of being a young woman in the presence of a young man.

"You! Of all people!" she was saying excitedly. "Mother and I have just arrived on the night train! Father is here to meet us. He and she seem to be so delighted to see each other that they are forgetting all about the porter, and which is our luggage and which isn't. So I thought the best thing I could do would be to follow him. There he is over there waiting, poor thing! You see—" suddenly she stopped. Her eyes had fixed themselves upon the band of black on James's arm. They moved to his tie, then upwards to meet his own. "Doctor? Who? Not your Father?"

"I wrote you a letter."

"I must have missed it." Slowly she put out her hand to touch him, then the eyes still looking up into his filled, overflowed and she turned aside. His father! What did one say at such a moment? Her life, carefree so far, had taught her nothing about this. And yet she wanted, desperately, to let him know how she felt for him! "Oh, what am I to say to you, Doctor James? You see I've never—"

"Never you heed, Miss Gailes. You don't need to say anything."

She caught his hand. "But I *am* sorry! You must believe how sorry I am!"

He smiled down upon her. And his own eyes in turn became misty. "I'll believe you. But never heed me. I'm fine." Over her shoulder he caught sight of two familiar figures. "There's your father and mother, Miss Gailes. Goodbye."

"But Doctor! No. All right. I'll write you at the hospital."

"I'm at Kinaldie now."

"All right. To there then."

Next day he got her letter.

MY DEAR DOCTOR JAMES,

Whatever am I to say to you after my idiotic behavior this morning? You were kind to me and told me it was all right. And that you understood how I felt about you. But how could you, when I just stood there in front of you, talking nonsense? But the letter about your father had missed me and the sudden news gave me a shock.

Forgive your terribly inadequate friend. But believe her when she says how dreadfully unhappy she is for you! I have only to think of losing my own father to know how you must feel!

[137]

Write to me and tell me all about yourself and everything you are doing. You somehow looked so long-legged and anxious and lost, this morning, that I can't get the sight of you out of my head and am spending the rest of the day worrying my head off about you. How are you, really? I must hear at once! Everything!

I wanted this to be a wonderful letter. Now on reading it through, I find it doesn't say what I mean at all.

God bless and keep you, Doctor James.

Ever,
CHARLOTTE

Constance sat watching James as he finished reading this, then folded it up slowly. Their eyes met and he smiled a little dazed smile, as he stood up to go on his morning rounds.

"Are you all right, Bruce?"

"Perfectly. Didn't sleep much. That's all."

"Nothing else wrong?"

"Nothing whatever, Mother."

Nothing, except that wilful self-deception and dour self-persuasion could not do any more for her stepson. These two had done their best to help him with his battle yesterday, and again through the waking hours of last night. But now he must acknowledge himself beaten.

Young James Mennock knew he was hopelessly, unreasonably in love with Charlotte Gailes.

CHAPTER THIRTEEN

I

Two evenings later, Walter Lyndoch came to Huntly Gardens. He felt tired a little and, as a consequence of this, was arguing with himself whether he would be justified in drinking a glass of whisky and soda when he got in. A glass, that was, additional to the one he allowed himself as a matter of routine when he dined alone with his wife. Without undue struggle, Walter decided he would be justified. Yet, justification or no justification, it would be better, he felt, if he could get to the decanter and the gasogene before Bertha became aware of his presence in the house.

Reassurance met him as he fumbled for his key. Sounds came down to tell him that Bertha was at her piano. Music then would cover on his arrival any noise he might happen to make in the dining room immediately beneath her.

Walter took no risks. Without even taking off his hat, he went straight in and helped himself. Having done so, he took his glass into the cloakroom with him. Now he could take off his overcoat, run water, cough and bang about as he pleased. The deed was done. His wife could now do nothing but accept the accomplished fact.

And presently, fortified by a gulp or two, he was making his way upstairs. Bertha's reception of him was disappointing. She merely looked up for a moment, saw that it was he, then bent once more, powerful and concentrated, over the massiveness of the Waldstein Sonata, playing the movement to the end.

When it was finished, she turned round on the piano stool and remarked: "So that's what you're up to, is it? Well, I suppose if you want to get fatter than you are—I've just been reading that alcohol is a great help if you're trying to put on weight." Her tone was amused and casual, making Walter feel that he and his self-indulgence were little things after all. Not worth a sharp reproof, even. Was his wife losing interest in him, he wondered?

Bertha rose, shut the piano and took an envelope from the mantelpiece. "Walter," she said, "here's a letter from young James Mennock. Pages of it. It's in confidence; to both of us. I don't know what to do."

"Do? What about?"

She took the sheets from the envelope and threw them down beside Walter, who now sat on the sofa drinking his whisky a little defensively.

"I wish I had kept out of this." Bertha began to walk about.

Walter picked up the closely written sheets, contracted his eyebrows at them, blinked, patted the pocket of his waistcoat where he kept his spectacles, found they were not there, put the sheets down again impatiently and said: "My dear woman, will you please tell me what this is about. What do you wish you had kept out of?"

Bertha turned. "James has fallen in love—or so he thinks."

"Thinks? He's twenty-four or -five. Why not? Who with?"

"You had better read the letter."

"No. I've got my whisky to drink and I've left my specs in my overcoat."

His wife stood considering an instant before she summarized: "The letter begins—well, just asking if he can come up and talk to us. Then it looks as if he couldn't keep the flood back; and down it all goes, pages of it, as you can see. It's that Mackinnon Gailes girl. He hates her parents and they hate him, and he doesn't know how things are going to be for himself, or Connie, or anybody! Poor James! But now he finds he's mad about her and what is he to do?"

Walter looked into his tumbler thoughtfully and with some regret that the tide was ebbing so quickly. "Dear me," he said helpfully. "What else?"

"Well—now she's home. He met her by chance. And she was wonderfully sympathetic about Peter's death. And she's more grownup now and the most beautiful child that ever— Oh, you know the sort of thing. Really, Walter, why won't you read the letter for yourself?"

Her husband ignored this. He swallowed the remainder of his drink, then turned for consolation to look at the pinafored girls in the Hornel painting. Thoughtfully, by means of a corner of the frame and his hands, he had isolated one who had strayed from the group to pick an outlying primrose. He was wondering if she would make a nice picture just by herself.

"Really, Walter! I wish you would stop that and listen to me! Please try to help!"

[140]

"I *am* trying. I'm busy thinking." He lowered his hands, turned back and looked at her. "But why see any difficulties in the way? Marriage into a rich university family would be the very thing for Jimmie. Everybody knows he is as bright as a bee."

"I wish you would try to understand the complications! He doesn't even know if she's in love with him!"

"Well, he had better find that out. You had better have a party. You know the girl, don't you? What's wrong with that idea?"

"Everything, Walter! Everything in the world! I hear dinner going in. Perhaps I'll get some sense out of you when you've had it!" Walter trying and Walter not trying, Bertha told herself with exasperation, were two different people.

But after dinner Walter did try; that is, if trying means sitting up solemn and alert, listening to what Bertha had decided for herself and giving his assent to it.

Satisfied now with her own and her husband's good sense, Bertha sat down to write James a letter. They were surprised, she wrote affectionately, at what had happened. Yet proud of course that James should turn to them in his all too obvious dilemma. His Uncle Walter and she had spent the whole of this evening thrashing out his problem. And here was the decision they had come to.

James must wait. Surely he could do that, couldn't he, if he really loved Charlotte? He must remember she was absurdly young and probably thought of him only as a friend. A year might make all the difference. They both felt that hurry would certainly be fatal. Let him go on playing the role of good friend during the next year or more and by that time everything might be different. The skies, if Bertha might offer the experience of an old woman as comfort, had a wonderful way of clearing.

In the meantime they would be delighted to see James in Glasgow in the near future to have a good talk. And they were, very sincerely, James's affectionate uncle and aunt.

Bertha blotted her letter and showed it to Walter who had now got his spectacles. Wisdom, he said, returning it to her, had never expressed itself better. After this encouragement, Bertha reread it herself, sealed it, and asked him to ring the bell that it might be taken to the post.

But Walter did not hear her. He had fallen asleep in his chair.

Professor Mackinnon Gailes looked up from the German monograph he was reading. "What's *Barmherzigkeit,* Edie?"

"Charity."

"But how can spiders be charitable?"

"I haven't the least idea."

"But can't *Barmherzigkeit* mean something quite different?"

"No. Not essentially different."

"Queer." The professor bent his thick eyebrows once again over the long and complicated German sentence that contained this word. "Good! Thank you very much! I've got it!" He laughed in triumph, scratched his cheek, shook himself, then settled down once more to his reading.

His wife laid down her book and looked pensively towards the window. In the gathering dusk, the rain was falling heavy and straight. The sight of it depressed her. A Scotch July evening. With a sigh she turned to look into the fire she had caused to be lighted in her husband's study, taking what comfort she could from the sight of it.

From above there came the sound of diligent piano practice. From that too Edith took some comfort. Since Charlotte had returned home until this evening she had not, even at her mother's request, consented to touch the piano. Edith sat listening. Yes. The child was playing better. The money they had paid to an expensive teacher had not, after all, gone for nothing. She continued to listen. Yes. Charlotte seemed to be playing very well. But why this sudden fit of practicing? And tonight particularly?

Edith looked across at her husband. His face and beard glowed warm in the firelight. Now and then the lines about his eyes crinkled into a half-smile and his lips moved, as they helped his mind to grope towards the sense of what he was reading. Edith wished she could meet and resolve her own difficulties as easily and with a like pleasure.

Although she could not quite give a name to these difficulties, she felt depressed and disappointed. For months she had looked forward to her daughter's homecoming. What they would do together. How, now that Charlotte was to all intents grownup, they would be close and delightful companions. But somehow things were not working out in that way. She had heard complaints from other mothers about other daughters. But surely these women had not taken the trouble to understand their girls as she understood Charlotte? She had always been able, she told herself, to read the child like a book.

Once more Edith sighed. The young woman who had come back to them was moody and elusive. At one moment accepting the affection of her parents without bothering to respond to it; the next, responding too emotionally. It was puzzling and somehow disquieting. Should she ask Charlotte's father what he thought? But Henry's simplicity had ever been blind to any flaw in their daughter. No. He was too happy, too untroubled. It was time he gave her his help.

"And what's *Zumvorscheinkommen?*"

"No, put down your book, Henry. I want to talk to you."

"But, Edie—"

"No, Henry, I'm worrying about Charlotte. Tell me what you think of her now that we have her home again."

"Think? What an extraordinary question! I think she's older, much more grownup; promises to be—is now—a very presentable young woman. But we're agreed on all this already."

"But now that we've had her for a fortnight. Haven't you noticed anything? Don't you find her moody or—I don't know—less approachable perhaps?"

The professor looked across at his wife, considering. Women were extraordinary creatures. Diving beneath the surface on the smallest provocation to fish up ridiculous trifles. "Approachable? As we become adult, my dear, we become in a way less approachable, more reticent, I daresay. We have a stronger sense of identity, of belonging to ourselves."

"To the extent of shutting out, of disobliging the people we live with?"

"Now what does that mean? I can't imagine Charlotte—"

"No, Henry. Of course you can't. What I mean is—" Edith stopped, found her illustration and went on: "Well, listen to her playing. I've wanted her to play ever since she came home. She talked about being too self-conscious or some such nonsense. Now listen to her! Would you call that behavior obliging?"

"She's playing very well, I should say."

"Yes. But why not before now? Why not when I asked her?"

"Shyness, Edie."

"Rubbish! When was Charlotte ever shy?"

Charlotte's father sat reflecting. No. He had seldom known her to be shy. Quite the reverse. She wouldn't be his daughter without her gay, rather simple overconfidence. How was he to defend her to her mother? "Well, perhaps not shy. But—" Now a thought had struck him. "By the way, Edie, when I was walking with Charlotte after church yesterday, we met that musical woman you took her to play to before she went away. You know, large, arty sort of person."

"Mrs. Lyndoch?"

"Yes, Lyndoch. Didn't you want her advice? She asked, of course, how Charlotte had got on. Charlotte offered to play for her."

"Offered?"

"Well, asked if she might come one day."

"And for me she won't even—"

The professor held up one hand to restrain his wife's quick annoyance while he ran the other through his mane distractedly. "My dear, I was only giving you that as a reason for her beginning to practice! That's all."

"And why, will you please tell me, should she offer to play for Mrs. Lyndoch, and yet refuse to play for her own mother?"

III

To this question Edith was, perhaps, the last person to receive the right answer. She asked Charlotte, of course.

Charlotte's reply was a smile and a reiteration that her mother, expecting too much, always made her nervous. Which Edith only half believed. Thereafter Charlotte actually did sit down and play for her, however, restoring some of Edie's good humor.

But why shouldn't she offer to play for Mrs. Lyndoch, the girl had demanded. Hadn't Mrs. Lyndoch been helpful before she had gone to Switzerland? And might not Mrs. Lyndoch, herself so accomplished, be able to help her further?

Although it was not quite the familiar Charlotte speaking, this seemed sensible enough. Besides, were not the diligent hours now spent at the piano much better than the moods and mooning that had gone before? Exhorting herself, therefore, to have patience with her daughter's growing up, her mother gave her consent to the visit.

But Edith's first feelings had been right. Charlotte was withdrawn and unlike herself. She was troubled over the young doctor of Kinaldie. Wherein had she failed him? Had she seemed unfriendly when they met at the station on the morning of her coming home?

Had the surprise at seeing him and hearing the news of his father's death made her manner seem cold to him somehow? He had taken almost a week to answer her letter.

Now in her room, as she made herself ready to walk down through Hillhead to Huntly Gardens, Charlotte took James's much-thumbed answer from the book in which she had hidden it and read it yet again.

My dear Miss Gailes,

Please forgive me if I did not reply to your letter of sympathy immediately. But I have been very busy arranging up father's affairs and taking over his work down here. I have had no time to write to anybody.

And please don't blame yourself for anything. It certainly did not cross my mind that you were behaving "idiotically." I felt it was very kind of you to worry about me at all, and I was very glad indeed to see you at the station the other morning.

You ask what I am doing. I am settling down as quickly as I can and trying to give all my time and interest to my work. There is no other choice.

Take care of yourself.

Yours in friendship,
James Mennock

P.S. Wouldn't it be queer if, the next time we saw each other, you were a stiff lady in a feather boa who didn't recognize the old, fat doctor with the bald head and the gold watch chain across his middle? J.M.

Where had her Doctor James gone to? Where was the teasing, amused writer of the letters to Lausanne? In the postscript? But even the postscript lacked warmth. What did he mean?

At first she had been very angry; angry at the stilted thanks, the cut-and-dried phrases. This was not her Doctor James.

She had sat down at once and put her annoyance on paper, demanding the reason for this cold, dismissing tone. Then, when she had sent it, reaction had come. By the same post she had written him another, begging his pardon, calling herself ill-mannered, pleading her anxiety about him and asking his forgiveness.

To these letters there had been no reply whatever! And she had sent them more than ten days ago. Charlotte was distracted. What could have happened? She must find out somehow. But how? Who could tell her? There was no one she could ask. She could not think of anyone who knew him.

And then, quite by chance, walking in Great Western Road in the after-church parade, she and her father had seen Bertha Lyndoch with her husband on the opposite pavement.

She left the professor's side and darted across the wide road. She would question them. James had more than once mentioned the Lyndochs in his letters.

Now as she made her way up Huntly Gardens, Charlotte thought of that encounter. What a fool she must have looked! She had stopped, panting, before two very surprised people. "Mrs. Lyndoch?"

"Yes?" For a moment Mrs. Lyndoch looked puzzled, then a smile had spread and a hand gone out. "Oh, I'm sorry. Of course I know you! You came to play to me before you went to Switzerland last autumn. This is my husband. Charlotte Gailes, Walter. You've heard me speak about her."

Why had Mr. Lyndoch given her his plump hand with such courtly enthusiasm? Was it his idea of good manners? "Oh, yes, I've heard about you! It's you who—"

Why had Mrs. Lyndoch turned sharply, laid a firm hand on his arm and taken his words determinedly from him? "Of course, Walter. Who went to Switzerland as I'm saying. How nice of you to come and speak to us, my dear. And did you like being there?"

But, standing before the Lyndochs, she had suddenly been overcome by a new shyness. A shyness she had not counted upon. She had intended, having run across the street, to cry out something like: "Oh, Mrs. Lyndoch! You know Doctor James Mennock, don't you? What *can* be wrong? Is he ill? He won't answer my letters! And I don't know what to do!" But now, this sudden shyness—this sense of shame, it almost seemed—forbade his name coming to her lips. Instead, she found herself stammering "In Switzerland? Very much, thank you. I liked it very much indeed."

"And the piano-playing? Did you go to the teacher I had thought of for you?"

"Oh yes. That—that's what I came across to tell you. Yes. I went to him. People think I am playing much better."

"Good, my dear. I'm glad about that."

But the Lyndochs had begun to look like moving away now, and the professor, bewildered at first by her sudden dart from his side, had marked her in the distance and was bearing down from across the road. Charlotte looked about her distractedly. She could not leave the Lyndochs like this. She must know about James. They were the only ones who might, perhaps, tell her.

She took her courage into her hands. "Oh—Mrs. Lyndoch."

"Yes?"

"Do you think— Would you allow me to play for you some time? Just to see—I feel it would—?"

"Of course, my dear! I'll be most interested. Come one afternoon. Let me see? Wednesday? And play for me before tea? I'll be alone. This must be your father looking for you."

Now having rung the doorbell, Charlotte stood waiting, terrified by her own audacity. How had she ever dared to propose coming here to exhibit her poor tinklings to such as Mrs. Lyndoch?

"Miss Gailes?" Charlotte realized that the door now stood open and that a maid was addressing her. "Would you just come in, please. Mrs. Lyndoch said I was to tell you she went out for her lunch and might be a wee thing late." The woman led Charlotte upstairs to Bertha's music room. "And Mrs. Lyndoch said would you please excuse her, and that you would mebbe like to practice your tunes till she gets back?"

IV

And so it happened that as James Mennock came up Huntly Gardens, sounds of piano-playing that he took to be Bertha's came down to him from the open window.

At later times, looking back on these, his first two meetings with Charlotte after her return from Switzerland, James was to marvel at how much fate had played its part in their coming together. First on that morning of her homecoming. And now this afternoon in the Lyndochs' house.

As he stood waiting for the door to open, he was glad. Glad that Bertha was at home. For he judged she would be alone and was playing to herself as was so much her custom. He wanted to talk to her. To ask her what next he had better do; to tell her how, in reply to his own, honorably cool letter, a letter such as Bertha had advised, he had at once received two from Charlotte, the first petulant and angry, the second meekly begging his forgiveness. He had hurt Charlotte and he could not bear it.

Then, when the front door did open, fate played yet another card.

The opener of the door was about to tell him that her mistress was not here and that it was a young lady awaiting her return who was playing in the music room. But at this moment the telephone, fixed in the front hall as were all telephones in the young century, began to ring with the crude and earsplitting fierceness of these early instruments, causing Bertha's parlormaid to jump and turn in panic to take up the receiver.

James flung down his hat and ran upstairs. He certainly did not stop to note that the music coming from above was made by lighter, less certain fingers than usual.

He halted at the door he had flung open. The head and shoulders, there against the light, belonged to some young girl. They did not belong to Bertha Lyndoch. Then he saw that it was Charlotte. He closed the door and remained, standing before it. "Miss Gailes!"

"Doctor James!" She stood up but did not move from before the keyboard.

It was a moment of trembling bewilderment for each of them; a bewilderment which neither made efforts to disguise.

"I didna know you would be here," James said, groping for mere words.

"I invited myself. I wanted to know if Mrs. Lyndoch thought my playing had improved." Then, suddenly ashamed of her untruthfulness, Charlotte added: "No. That's nonsense. I only made my playing an excuse."

Dazed, he came forward into the room. "Excuse? Excuse for what?"

She had left the piano without replying and was standing in front of him.

"I'm sorry, Miss Gailes. Why should I be asking what's none of my business?" He was turning aside when he felt her hand upon his arm and heard her cry:

"But it *is* your business! I wanted to see Mrs. Lyndoch. She was the only person who could tell me what was wrong with you! If you were ill! Your last letter was so— And then I wrote you those two silly ones! But you didn't answer them. You didn't do anything! You just—"

The hand that clung to James's own, the large brimming eyes that kept on seeking to hold his own, the hot uprush of his feelings, had almost overcome him. Yet for a time James Mennock's resolution continued glumly with its fight. This child meant everything, of course. But Charlotte was so young. And he himself was not yet ready. And though, indeed, he must by now know her heart was given to him, he still would not admit it. No words of love had ever passed between them. In a sense they hardly knew each other. They had been together so little. And her parents? Yes, her parents. "They don't want me!" He muttered those words grimly, more than once, quite unconscious that he spoke aloud. "They don't want me!" It was a mere externalizing of his struggle.

"What is it? Who doesn't want you?"

He turned to look down at her. "I was put out of their house! And when she came to the hospital she wouldna look at me!"

"What house? Who is *she*?"

"Your mother." He caught her hand, caressing it nervously.

"Mother? I can't believe it! Mother would never—"

"I tell you, I was shown the door! That day I came to give your father back his money!" His tone was harsh. "Your father and mother think I'm mud!"

"Oh!" Charlotte gave a little cry of pain. She was weeping sorely now, shocked by what he said. She did not know that these angry words were not for her; were mere, bitter sparks thrown out from the battle. She disengaged her hand, took both of his into her own, and stood again searching his face, trying to understand him. "James! Tell me. Mother couldn't— I don't see why—!"

"Well, I can! It's not hard to see when you're not wanted!"

For a time she remained holding fast his hands, weeping and anxious, scanning his troubled face, a bewildered child. But at last the dawn of self-knowledge came, dispelling the mists of immaturity, breaking through slowly into an awe-struck, trembling half-smile.

He looked down wondering. Then he heard her cry out:

"James! James! No one must ever come between you and me! I can't bear that anything like that should be allowed to matter! Whatever anyone says or does, it mustn't matter!"

James's fight was over. Whether she had thrown herself into his arms at this, or whether he had caught her to him, neither of them would ever know.

But at all events, when in the next moment Bertha Lyndoch, panting for breath and hurrying to excuse her lateness, threw the door ajar, she found them thus together.

Which of the three was most dumfounded it would be difficult to say; the mistress of the house or the young couple, now drawing quickly apart. Bertha was not usually slow in handling situations, but at once the seriousness of this one began to press about her, blunting her decision. "James!" she found herself exclaiming, "I had no idea you were both coming here this afternoon!"

In deep embarrassment the young man looked anxiously at Charlotte, then he turned to face Bertha. "No. Nor I." And as his aunt said nothing to this, he looked once more at Charlotte and went on. "This wasna arranged. It just—well, you see what has happened."

"Yes. I see. So neither of you had any idea the other was to be here?"

"No."

"Or that—" She looked from one to the other.

"Or that we might get to where we've got to?" James asked.

Quite unaccountably, Bertha's eyes filled with tears. She went to Charlotte, took her into her arms and kissed her, then she pulled down James's hot, red face and kissed that too. "There," she said, taking refuge in her wonted brusqueness. "Tea will be up in about a quarter of an hour. I'll leave you to come to your senses until it comes."

If the truth were told, she was thankful to find herself in the high, airy room of grey and white that was her own and Walter's bedroom. Thankful to have breathing space. Thankful to have time to sit and think.

They had not, then, arranged to come here? It had all come about by chance. Or had that little minx invited herself, using her piano-playing as a pretext? Well, chance on James's side anyway.

Bertha took off her hat and sat down in front of her white dressing table to rearrange her hair. No. Charlotte's sin could not, even if she had schemed, be labeled scarlet!

At all events James had found her here; control had presumably given way and there they were! The letter that she, Bertha, had written to him some days ago advising restraint and patience had, it seemed, done nothing! What next?

In her Dresden days she had known of more than one explosive love affair. Music and freedom had encouraged such among her friends and fellow students. And most of these young couples had found their own solutions; which had been, of course, none of her business.

But this, happening in her house, *was* her business and Bertha was a daughter of her time and of her world. She knew its code and lived by it. How then did she herself stand in the face of what had happened? What must she say to these two children?

Lingering to make up her mind, Bertha finished her toilet so slowly that, as it was finished, she could hear the rattle of the tea tray.

They sat apart, awkwardness and confusion again made evident by her coming. But she saw too that these things were on the surface; that a shining happiness had taken hold of them.

She was glad to have the refuge of the tea table, glad to have something to do while she talked. "Well? And what am I to say to you now?" The dryness of this question did not conceal goodwill.

"We want your help, Aunt Bertha," James said.

"You seem to have done pretty well without it already!"

"Advice, then."

Bertha took her time, performing the rites of the tea table with deliberation. "There," she said, "drink that, and eat some bread and butter. And tell me first what you think of doing. I take it that you now consider yourselves engaged to be married?" And when they nodded: "Well? What next?" And again receiving no other answer than embarrassment: "It seems to me that Charlotte's parents—I'm calling you Charlotte and I'll stick to Charlotte—that Charlotte's parents will have to be told at once."

She was not surprised by the alarm on their faces. Charlotte turned in panic to James, while James looked in confusion from Charlotte to Bertha herself.

"Well? What else is there to do? How else are you going to see each other? A busy country doctor, who has not even had time to find his feet yet, won't find much free time to come to Glasgow and serenade you at your window? Will he? And a young girl of your kind, Charlotte, who is—how old?"

"Nearly eighteen." Charlotte spoke with spirit, a spirit that lit up her face and pulled at the older woman's heartstrings.

"How can you, Charlotte, have hole and corner meetings with James in other people's houses or anywhere else, and keep these meetings from your parents? Oh, you needn't think you're going to go on seeing Charlotte in this house, James! There are to be no secret meetings here! What kind of creature would Professor and Mrs. Gailes think I was if I allowed them? And what kind of person would they think you were?"

"I know what they think about me already," he said bitterly. "And so do you. I've told you."

Bertha nodded. "That doesn't make it any easier does it?" Then, seeing their despondency, she forced a laugh. "Oh, don't look so miserable! When Charlotte's parents find out what kind of young man you are, I'll be surprised if they don't count themselves lucky to have you in the family! If only all this had happened in, say, two years from now." Bertha was well aware that sentiment was speaking, not conviction. Yet how could she be severe with these poor children? "And remember your Uncle Walter and I are always willing to help where we can. Only nothing secret, please!"

She sat back and took up her own teacup, watching them with more sympathy than she dared show, then added: "When you've finished, Charlotte, you had better take out some music and play it to me, so that I can tell your mother, when I meet her, that I've heard you playing."

CHAPTER FOURTEEN

I

It was after eleven when James got home to Kinaldie. He had quitted Bertha Lyndoch's house with Charlotte soon after tea. They had found a place to talk in that part of the Botanic Gardens that slopes abruptly down to the river Kelvin; a secluded region where the paths are steep and winding and darkly overhung by trees. Here on a bench they had spent an hour. Talking together shyly, happily awkward towards each other in the presence of their love.

As he came from the railway station into the summer darkness, James was surprised to find that the pony trap which stood there with its lamps lit, waiting, was his own. Why? When home was a mere ten minutes away?

"Hello, Davie," he said to his stable boy, standing by the pony's head, "anything wrong? Has somebody been looking for me? I ought to have been back sooner, but I couldn't get away."

"Ah've had this pauny in harness since five o'clock," the boy answered glumly.

"I'm sorry, Davie. Who is it?"

"An' Ah've come tae meet a' the trains!"

"Oh, all right! But tell me who it is, damn you!" James was surprised by his own sudden anger, by the sharp pitch of voice. He must take hold of himself. When he spoke again he had forced his tone to drop to normal. "I'm tired, Davie. Tell me who wants me."

"They're expecting a wean at Dunardoch." This was the name of an outlying farm. "Dunardoch cam doon himsel' aboot five o'clock and said that his mistress had stertit."

"I wish she had started at a more sensible time!" James' answer was dreary. He felt in the darkness of the trap for his doctor's bag, found it, opened it under a station lamp, saw what he needed was there, then jumped in and took up the reins. "Thanks, Davie. You can get away home. But go to Gowan Bank first and tell Mrs. Mennock where I've gone and not to wait up for me. I may be all night."

He called to the pony, then turned its head towards the country. Why, tonight of all nights, should his rest be denied him?

And yet, presently, James felt pleased to be up here among the sleeping farm lands driving through the bland summer night. His eyes, now become accustomed, were finding the darkness merely half-darkness. All around and above him stars pricked the heaven's deep blue with points of light. Except in the north where the sun, spending a few short hours behind the outline of the hills, had left a cold twilight on the horizon. It was not difficult to find his way, or rather for his beast to find it for him. Here in a quiet broken by rhythmic hoofclaps, by the single cry of a moor bird, by the distant bark of a fox, or again by the sudden startled rustle of some unseen creature as his lamps swept the hedges, James felt refreshed, felt the tensions of the day receding, felt his mind more clear.

Bertha Lyndoch's words came back to him. "If only all this had happened in, say, two years from now!" Bertha was indeed right, in the light of his own problems here at Kinaldie; and of Charlotte's youth and irresponsibility.

She had wanted to bring him to her parents, insisting that all objection must melt at the sight of their happiness. This, of course, he would not do. Well then, she must tell them when she got home, as Mrs. Lyndoch had counseled, and he would see how at once everything would come straight. He had made her promise not to do that either. He would meet her again next week, he had said. He must have time to think. But where? Here, down by the Kelvin? Anywhere. But how? she had asked. What excuse could she give for going out? He had said that they must think of one.

James could see a faroff light now. It was moving back and forth before the white wall of a building. That must be Dunardoch Farm. Someone was there, flashing a stable lamp, watching with impatience for the doctor. He hoped his own faint lights were strong enough to carry reassurance to the watcher. He bent over to look at them. Small white moths and night flies fluttered across their yellow beams. James sat back and called encouragement to the pony.

Then suddenly Charlotte had exclaimed with delight at the thought of an intrigue. Of course she would find a way! She would invite herself back to Mrs. Lyndoch's, saying she must play to her again! No, he said. The Lyndochs must be asked to do nothing. Well, she would contrive something else. James would see. And she would write to him every day. Oh, and by the way, he had better enclose *his* letters in an envelope addressed to one of her mother's maids. Charlotte would give the girl warning. And wasn't it splendid to be doing anything so romantic?

Charlotte's mischievous look, her eyes as she said this, came back to James as he drove on towards that faroff light. There, under those trees in the Botanic Gardens, he had found himself gathering this naughty child into his arms with a sudden new rage in his senses that had alarmed him. Yet his lowland blood hated the thought of intrigue of any kind—intrigue, however innocent.

Now the stable lamp was drawing nearer. It was coming towards him, lighting the way for running footsteps which presently he could hear upon the road.

Some moments later a voice called: "Is that the doctor?"

"Hello! Is that Dunardoch, himself?"

"Aye, it's me, Doctor."

"How's your mistress?"

"The bairn's here!"

"What? Born already? And is your wife all right?"

"I hope so. I think so. Her mother was wi' her and a byrewoman."

The young farmer stood panting by the side of the trap now. "They put me ootside the door, and that's where I had to stay. Yon's terrible, Doctor!" But there was neither distress nor shock in the robust grinning face.

"A first baby, Dunardoch. You'll be used to all that by the tenth! What have you got? A boy or a girl?"

The man's grin widened, showing his strong teeth. "A boy!"

James laughed. "Fine! The next farmer of Dunardoch Farm! He'll be putting you out and taking your place one of these days, man! But I'm sorry I wasn't with your wife. I was kept in Glasgow. We didn't expect the baby so soon, did we?"

It was two o'clock when James had finished with the young mother and her child. He came back into the farm kitchen; to eat and drink the lavish simplicity that had been left for him, then to sit in the farmer's chair by a fire, blazing high and quite unnecessary on such a warm night. The farm collies, uneasy at his unwonted presence, moved about grumbling, refusing to settle down in their usual corners. He was left to munch his scones and drink his tea by himself. Everyone, it seemed, had gone to lie down for the short remaining hours of summer darkness.

Charlotte! Suddenly, hotly, his troubled heart was crying out for

Charlotte! His very exhaustion was crying out for Charlotte! No. He must take hold of himself. She was too young. He must wait. He must have patience. Indeed, he must have wisdom for two, and tell her that they must, both of them, have patience. It was only fair —to her and to himself. And now he must try to be calm and sit here in the warmth and stillness, soberly considering, planning what next he had better do.

Some minutes later the farmer found James fast asleep. He was lying back, loose and weary, there in the chair; his pale face and his glinting red hair caught in the light of the kitchen fire. Making sure no burning coal would fall, Dunardoch called softly to his dogs; then, closing the door without noise, he left the young doctor to rest.

II

In the months that followed, Charlotte continued to puzzle and disappoint her mother. Edith could make nothing of her. Where was the Charlotte of the old days? Where was the gentle child, lighthearted and gaily frivolous, of the days before Lausanne?

The professor tried to reassure his wife by insisting that their daughter was fast growing up; that the coming of womanhood with its self-realizations and discoveries was, just for the moment, upsetting and bewildering her, and that presently the Charlotte they knew would re-emerge.

But Edith could not quite believe that. Other girls of Charlotte's age did not seem to withdraw themselves like this; did not behave, now and then, as though something weighed upon them; as though, almost, they had something to hide. But these suspicions were, of course, ridiculous! What could this much-protected, much-adored child have or want to hide? There had been this prank in the exhibition park with that odd young doctor more than a year ago. Yet that had been mere childish overconfidence, foolish and innocent, and no harm had come of it. Last summer, certainly, while they were traveling, she had insisted upon sending him one or two postcards. But now Edith was glad she had let her do so. Charlotte's interest in him had, it seemed, proved, as she had hoped, to be nothing more than a schoolgirl enthusiasm and had died a natural death. Besides, there had never been any sign that the young man had ever bothered to reply. Edith had not failed to keep an eye on the

[156]

letters. But none had come bearing the Kinaldie postmark. Nor had Charlotte shown any sign of wanting to keep letters from her.

The summer passed. The Mackinnon Gailes family had spent some weeks of August and September at Braemar among the glories of Deeside, where Charlotte had without fatigue gone for long walks with her father or climbed the high mountains in the company of other young men and women; a proof, at least, that her body was sound, whatever the cloud upon her spirits.

Then in late September, whenever they were home again the child had at once taken up her piano-playing, showing determination and an astonishing interest. Astonishing, since, as her mother was aware, her talent was not above the average. Edith could only conclude that in Switzerland Charlotte had been in the hands of a gifted teacher who knew how to kindle enthusiasm in his pupils. At all events there was some comfort to be taken from this diligence and from the fact that Charlotte had begged them to let her have lessons from a teacher of high reputation in the town, and had now taken to spending a surprisingly large part of every Wednesday afternoon at his house.

Late autumn. Charlotte's birthday. December. Christmas. New Year. Relationships had shaken down in the Mackinnon Gailes household. The new different Charlotte had come to be accepted. The Charlotte who was cheerful enough, perhaps, yet who somehow behaved too carefully now, who seemed somehow to have lost that inconsequent charm that had been so much a part of the old one.

Then suddenly, in mid-January, the storm broke.

Edith was sewing by a piled-up fire in the professor's study, regretting the arrival of frost and wishing that both he and his daughter might reappear so that they could all have tea. She was pleased when she heard the front door bang, then her husband's heavy tread as he crossed the hall to take off his overcoat.

"Hello, Edie. Very cold outside. And fog. Ring for tea, will you?"

He had come in, laid what looked to his wife very much like Charlotte's music case upon his work desk and was now standing, his back to the fire, the tails of his frock coat raised the better to heat the behind part of his massive person. "Where's the child?"

"It's her music day."

"Wednesday! I quite forgot! I took her music case without asking her. It was on the piano, empty, so I grabbed it forgetting she would want it. I was in a hurry and couldn't find anything to put some lecture notes in! Ha! Here's tea!"

"Please. On the Professor's desk," Edith said, giving instructions. She placed herself on her husband's revolving chair and began pouring out for him.

"Thanks, Edie!" Still standing before the fire, he took his cup, made to drink it at a gulp, discovered it was hot, then coughed and laid it behind him on the mantelpiece. "Give me a muffin," he said crossly, then recovering himself exclaimed: "Oh that reminds me! I said it was empty, but it wasn't quite. Give me it over, my dear."

Edith reached across for it.

Her husband put what remained of his muffin on his saucer and bent to open his daughter's music case. "There was a photograph of Charlotte in it. One I had never seen. I didn't have time to look at it. I pulled it out in class. So I had to put it back at once. But I saw it was Charlotte all right. I've only just remembered. Yes, here it is. Where are my glasses?"

While her husband was making a tour of his pockets, Edith took it from him, drew it from the envelope that contained it and held it beneath the light. Yes. This was Charlotte. Excellent of the child, really. Or had the photographer made her look too old? But why had she gone to have this taken? And why hadn't she told them? Odd child. To the exacerbation of her husband's patience, Edith held it in her hand, looking at it this way and that, pondering. Finally she turned it over. "Henry!"

"Edie, what is it?"

"Look. Look at that! Read it!"

Adjusting his spectacles and bending over her he read: "For my very dearest husband-to-be, James Bruce Mennock. From his devoted Charlotte Mackinnon Gailes." The Professor straightened himself and stood looking about him bewildered and fierce. "Well? We haven't been left in any doubt about their intentions, have we?" he said at length. And then, seeing his wife's handkerchief was out: "Now, Edie—no! Look here! Don't do that. We'll—we'll get all this put straight, you know. The thing's absurd on the face of it! She's only a schoolgirl."

They heard the outside door.

"There she is!" Edith started, swung round in the swivel chair and caught her husband's hand. "Henry! What are we to do?"

"Steady, Edie! Look; leave the photograph out. We'll see what the poor child has to say."

Charlotte had been anxious and annoyed at the disappearance of her music case, not that she wasn't forever forgetting where she had put it. But with that signed photograph in it! And she had meant to surprise James with it today. Still the case must be somewhere and why should anyone look inside it? But her anxiety was not diminished by the sight of her parents.

"Charlotte, I took that this morning, I didn't remember you would need it."

She winced.

She had heard her father speak in these tones to others, but never to herself. She stood now, feeling a sudden chill as her eyes fell on the case of soft leather lying beneath his study lamp. From there they moved and came to rest upon her own photograph, lying on the professor's blotting pad. She stood looking at it foolishly.

"We saw what was written on the back," her father's voice was saying.

Slowly she raised her eyes to his. There she found distress and severity. Her mother, still holding his hand, did not look at her.

Thus for a time they remained, neither moving nor speaking, these three who had known no feelings other than tenderness and a gentle, rather exclusive admiration, one for the other. Each in a different way was stunned by what had happened.

Presently Charlotte became aware that her mother was speaking low, muttering almost to herself: "It's the deceit of it, Charlotte. The thought that this has been going on and we didn't know."

Charlotte broke! She fell on her knees before her mother, hid her face in her lap and gave herself up to a storm of hysterical weeping.

But even while she remained thus, crying her heart out, with her mother's unhappy hands distractedly caressing her head, Charlotte became aware of other feelings. Mixed with sorrow at having caused her parents pain, she felt glad that, whatever now might happen, her love for James at last had come to light. These months of trick and subterfuge were over! And whose fault was it that James never came here? That he and she must meet each other secretly in parks and teashops like any couple from the street? Whose fault was it that they, her parents, should have no knowledge of the man he really was?

In time these thoughts brought her a measure of calmness. She drew herself away from her mother and rose to her feet. "I'm sorry to have made you so unhappy," she said.

Her father put an arm about her. "You've been meeting him and writing him letters, I daresay?" he asked.

She nodded.

"We won't ask you about wheres and hows, my dear. If you admit this has happened, it has happened. I see no point in asking vulgar questions. But the next step must be to have this young man here. You may be very fond of him, Charlotte, although I can't imagine how that should ever have happened. But he must be much older than you are, and the responsibility for this—this underhand behavior must be, in great part, his."

His daughter broke from his arm. "It's not! I assure you both it's not! I've done quite as much as James!"

Her father raised his heavy eyebrows, but his voice continued in calm severity: "That's as may be, Charlotte. But I must see Doctor Mennock as soon as possible. If he's a man at all he'll certainly come. And if he does come, he'll have to listen to what I think of him." The professor motioned to his wife. "Let me sit down at my desk, Edie. I'll write to him now, at once." He fumbled about, looking for notepaper. "Enticing a foolish schoolgirl into an affair like this! Even if you had been over twenty-one— Oh, go and wash your face, Charlotte, then come back and have your tea! I don't want to talk to you any more about this—this distasteful business, until I've seen the young man."

She did as she was told, and her father took up his pen while her mother recovered herself enough to marvel at his show of firmness.

Jean, the parlormaid, was given the professor's letter immediately it was written. But, while she was in the post office, she also sent a telegram containing the following words, cryptic, unsigned and unpunctuated: ARTICLE IN DISPUTE BELONGS TO YOU NOT TO THEM NO MATTER WHAT THEY SAY NEVER FORGET THIS.

"Sit down, Doctor Mennock, please."

Without taking off his thick winter overcoat, James laid aside his hat and placed for himself a chair on the other side of the professor's desk.

The elder man sat in his swivel chair, stretched his hands flat on the blotting pad in front of him, a habit of his in moments of tension, and said: "At least you came at once. I didn't expect you so soon. If at all."

" 'If at all,' Professor Gailes? Did you think I would be frightened to come?"

"I beg your pardon, Doctor Mennock. I shouldn't have said that. No, all I meant was that my letter had only been written after tea yesterday. You must have got it early this morning. It was good of you to come so soon."

"Thanks. But if you think I'm the kind of man to—"

Charlotte's father held up a hand to restrain this self-defensive, inflammable young man. "Please, Doctor Mennock. I think it would help both of us if we managed to keep calm."

"Calm! After what you wrote in your letter!"

Henry Gailes gave himself a moment before he obliged himself to reply: "It was a letter that had to be written, unfortunately. You had to be told we had found out you had a secret engagement to marry our daughter; that we were very distressed about it; and that we felt your conduct was dishonorable."

"Dishonorable!"

"Yes, dishonorable, Doctor Mennock! Charlotte is scarcely a woman yet. What right had you to—"

"What else could we be but secret, Professor Gailes? What would you have said to me if I had come to you last summer when the thing happened and—"

"Happened! What happened?"

James sat looking across at the professor with eyes that burned. "What was it you had in mind? Seduction? Thanks for your opinion of me!"

The professor ran a hand through the thickness of his mane, scratched a cheek, rubbed his nose, laid his hands flat once more upon his blotting paper to steady himself and turned his Jovelike head towards the window, looking up in troubled reflection at the winter sky. But he was not feeling in any way Jovelike. He was not quite sure what he was feeling like. Nor where he was getting to. "My opinion of you, Doctor Mennock? Oh no, I didn't mean to imply anything so dishonorable as seduction. Indeed, you may not be surprised to hear," he went on, "that since we discovered this yesterday, I *have* been doing my best to get an opinion of you; I have been doing my best to find out what sort of person you are. The medical people at the university were, of course, able to tell me. And at the Royal Infirmary. I think you'll admit, that for my daughter's sake, this wasn't just prying. Oh, don't be alarmed! I didn't bring Charlotte or ourselves into this. It was easy enough without that."

"And what kind of reports did you get?" James was still looking at him closely.

"Excellent. Couldn't have been better. Brilliant; hard-working; conscientious; wasting yourself down in the country. Which makes this—this foolishness quite—quite incomprehensible to me."

Now there was a note of relief, of pleading even, in James's voice as he said: "I didna like being forced to be secret, sir. I didna want this to happen for a year or two. You'll mebbe have heard that my father died. And I had to take his place in a hurry. And what with Charlotte being so young— Oh, I can tell you, I've nearly been out of my judgment!"

Henry Gailes knitted his brow. "You felt all that? Didn't want the engagement to happen? Yet you—? But why?"

"We couldna help it, sir. We met unexpectedly. Has Charlotte not told you? And—and what we felt got the better of us."

"No. No, I can't understand." The professor continued to look puzzled. "But what went before all this, Mennock? How—how were you—how did you get into this sympathy with each other?"

There were sounds outside and a moment later Edith Gailes came into the study pulling off her gloves She halted at the sight of James.

"Doctor Mennock is here, as you see," her husband was saying. "Come in and sit down, Edie."

She took her place mechanically by the fireside. Whatever her feelings she controlled them. She appeared to James impersonal and without emotion, as though she had merely arrived late at a committee meeting. Neither she nor he troubled to hold out a hand nor indeed to exchange any kind of greeting.

James regretted her coming. In his heart he could not dislike Charlotte's father. And just now it had looked as though the professor had been trying really to understand; trying to see reason. With Charlotte's mother James's feelings were different.

"Where's Charlotte?" the professor asked.

"She's not here," Edith answered shortly. The less said about their daughter's whereabouts before predatory young men the better.

This brought a pause. And in this pause the room seemed to grow colder. James did not feel it was for him to continue the discussion. Edith, having snapped its thread by her coming, waited to find out what they had been saying. Her husband could not for a time remember just where she had broken it.

But as the other two seemed to expect him to speak, the professor made the effort. "Doctor Mennock has just been telling me how upset he has been, Edie."

"Upset? Upset about what?" Her voice was brittle.

"Well, about this secret understanding, this—"

"I was trying to explain to Professor Mackinnon Gailes how I hadna wanted this to happen for a long time yet, Mrs. Gailes," James interposed. "Charlotte being so young. And I had just lost my father and was left with his practice on my hands."

"We never wanted it to happen at all. At any time," she said.

Her husband either did not hear or chose to ignore this. "What I can't understand—as I was saying when you came in, Edie—is: How did they ever get round to this? What had gone before, that, well, that they should feel themselves in love; that they should come to imagine they wanted to marry each other?"

James flushed with annoyance at this word spinning. "There was no imagination in it, sir! Charlotte and I have been promised man and wife since the end of last July. We had been writing all the winter before that when she was abroad. And then, when she got home; whenever we saw one another again— Anyway, we met in my aunt, Mrs. Lyndoch's house, and that was where it happened."

"Mrs. Lyndoch? So she's been helping? I didn't think—"

"You needna think anything, Mrs. Gailes! She wasna in the house even! And I had no idea Charlotte would be there either! I just came in and found her."

Edith flinched at this rough directness. But flinching would get her nowhere. And so she sat for a time, sending her mind back to that sudden fit of piano practice and Charlotte's eagerness to go to Mrs. Lyndoch. Pity she had ever taken the child to see that woman.

"I suppose Mrs. Lyndoch has gone on inviting you to meet there since?"

"Not once. She didna want us."

"Why?"

"She said we were not to come back till you and Professor Mackinnon Gailes had been told."

As his wife made no reply to this the professor said: "Wise woman." And the room relapsed into a hostile silence.

A silence that told James plainly that with Charlotte's mother there could be no way out. And yet he felt he must still try to find one. In desperation, he stood up to make his words more impressive.

"Professor and Mrs. Gailes, I love your daughter Charlotte and she loves me. It would be hard for us to lose one another now. If I've done what's wrong, I'm sorry. But if it was wrong, at least there's been no evil. And now what do you want me to do? I'll try to be reasonable. I promise you that. Why have you asked me to come here? What have you to say to me?"

"Well—" The professor sat back in his chair and again ran a puzzled hand through his mane.

But Charlotte's mother also rose to her feet. These were direct questions and the young man must be given direct answers. If her husband wouldn't then she must force herself to do it. "What is it we have to say to you, Doctor Mennock? We want to ask you to leave our daughter alone." Then in response to an angry gesture from James: "No, please! We wanted to make you see it was the only honorable thing to do. That she was absurdly young; that she couldn't possibly know her own mind; that you would only end in making her very unhappy; that she could never adjust to the people or the life you belong to."

"Thanks very much, Mrs. Gailes! And if I had been the Duke of Something would she still have been 'absurdly young'?"

"No, Doctor Mennock. You must try to understand this. Our daughter has lived a very sheltered life. Young girls of her kind are brought up like that. The child is impetuous and full of romantic ideas which have, I daresay, allowed her to deceive us; have allowed her to go on meeting you secretly. But we know our daughter better than you do, Doctor Mennock. And we know she is innocent and good."

"Good God, Mrs. Gailes! Do you think I don't know that too?"

"Edie—!"

"Well if you know it, Doctor Mennock, why lead a good child into —into this secrecy—these underhand ways?"

"We had to see one another, Mrs. Gailes. What kind of reception did I get up here? When I came I was shown the door! What happened when you saw me up at the Royal Infirmary? You looked through me!"

"I'm sorry if—"

"You just don't want me! Don't want me at all!"

She turned away from James' loud, wounded shouting, lowering her head as though his voice had struck her and supporting herself by laying her hand on the back of her husband's chair. When she spoke it was almost in a whisper and still with bent head. "No, Doctor Mennock. You are quite right. We just don't want you!"

Again there was silence in the room. A silence in which James stood, quivering and tense, trying to decide if it were worth the breaking. But at last he turned, took up his hat, hurled at them an angry "Goodbye!" and went.

The study door banged behind their troublesome visitor.

Edith covered her eyes and dropped back into the chair by the fireside.

Her husband continued to sit where he was, staring unhappily before him. They had managed this interview badly and perhaps without effect. They had reached no conclusions, extracted no promises. But Edie and he were not much good at this kind of thing.

He swung round in his chair and did his best to comfort her.

CHAPTER FIFTEEN

I

Margaret lay sucking the end of her pencil, reflecting over what she had just written in the foregoing chapter.

She was still in bed, though it was midmorning, recovering from a sharp cold. But the cold had been short as well as sharp. And thus only for two days had she been unfit to go on with her writing. Two days of impatience now that the characters concerned had come together with an impact that would carry this love story through to a finish.

As she must remain indoors she had, with Sir James's permission, sent her keys to the paragon, begging him to fetch such materials as she might need from Woodside Terrace. (She did not, of course, know that these keys had already been in the young man's hands.) Having come to James's fateful interview with Charlotte's parents, she could not rest until it was written down. Now, this morning, it was finished, and the scribbled sheets—scored, amended, and tangled as she had striven for truth and fairness—lay scattered on the cover before her.

Out of this battle, it was the figure of Edith that emerged to raise questions in Margaret's mind. She had tried to put herself in her great-grandmother's place. Tried to feel her shyness and pride, her restricted judgments, her tenderness and her love for her only daughter.

On reflection, Margaret did not think she had gone wrong in what she had written down. Yet she felt she had missed something. Was Edith Gailes an altogether larger person than she had so far considered her to be?

"Well, darling? How are you this morning?" Lady Mennock said, coming in.

"Much better, Granny. I'm getting up."

"Do you really think you ought? And have you been sitting up in bed writing since crack of dawn, you foolish creature?"

The foolish creature smiled. "Dawn doesn't crack very early at the end of February. I'm all right." And then without giving her time to pursue this sterile topic she asked: "Granny, what kind of person was your mother?"

"What kind of person? You've been asking me that all winter!"

"Yes. I know. But I was thinking about her just now and I was wondering how fit she was to meet a situation she loathed; to accept it and to make the best of it? Did she merely become distressed and intractable? I don't suppose she can have been the stiff, unpleasant person Grandfather makes her in his diaries?"

Charlotte Mennock, as her granddaughter had hoped, took the question seriously. This time she did not spring to an unconsidered defense of her mother. Margaret's eyes followed her tall figure as she took to pacing back and forth in the room. Ordinarily, her judgments of people did not go so deep as those of her husband. But his mother-in-law had ever been Sir James's blind spot. At last Lady Mennock turned, anchored herself at the foot of the bed and gave judgment, examining her feelings as she gave it.

"No. My mother didn't just become intractable and distressed when things went against her. I can think of many times, when I was a child, when it was my mother who stepped in to hold things together. It certainly was she who took the Keswick situation in hand."

Margaret started. Keswick? Her grandmother had never mentioned Keswick since they had looked at the honeymoon photograph together last autumn. Now, very soon, she would be reaching the flight to Keswick in her narrative.

But already Lady Mennock's thoughts had moved on. She stood abstracted, far off, lost, it seemed, in memory. Indeed, her next words were spoken almost as though she had forgotten Margaret's presence. "And all through my poor Sandy's difficulties, my mother was quite wonderful. I don't know what I should have done without her."

Again Margaret started. She had kept her New Year's promise to Sir James not to pry into any papers concerned with her father. But she had not promised she would not listen to her grandmother if she wanted to talk. "Was your mother with you when my father died?"

"Yes. She was with me when your grandfather had to go to London at the end."

But this question had brought Lady Mennock to the surface again. What next, her granddaughter wondered, must be said to hold her to the subject of her son? "Was your own mother very fond of my father, Granny?"

"Very. Yet I remember her scolding me about him. Telling me I spoilt him far too much."

"And did you?" Despite their innocence, Lady Mennock's words had somehow struck coldly in Margaret's ears.

"Oh, I daresay I did. How could I help it?"

II

But now Margaret felt she must at all costs encourage her grandmother to go on talking. The old lady, as she well knew, was quite capable of beginning a confidence, then drawing back. She turned to her bedside table and took up a large yellow envelope containing papers and scribbled notes. From this she withdrew a photograph. "I've never shown you this, Granny." It was the snapshot of her father standing on the springboard by the lake of Hallstadt.

Lady Mennock took it, found her spectacles, and carried it to the window. "Sandy! That must have been in Austria." For a long time she continued to linger over it. But at length she looked up. When she spoke her voice was unsteady. "Where did you get this, Margaret?"

"I found it in a letter, Granny."

"When? Recently?"

"No. Some months ago."

"Then why ever haven't you shown it to me before?"

"I wasn't sure if you would like to see it. I thought it might bring things back. You see, darling, neither you nor Grandfather have ever talked very much to me about my parents, have you? I came to the conclusion that his loss was still an open wound. Grandfather *did* speak of him some weeks ago and promised to tell me their story. But so far he hasn't and I haven't dared to bother him."

"No, Margaret. Don't bother him. He doesn't like even me to talk about his son. It would have been a help to me, I think, if we could have spoken freely after he was gone. But your grandfather seems to be one of those people who can't mention a sorrow. It's understandable." Charlotte Mennock's voice continued brittle as she went on: "He was called to London at the time your father and mother died. He was there at the end."

"Did my father and mother die about the same time, darling?"

[168]

"They died within a day of each other! There was an influenza epidemic in London."

"And was I in London with them?"

"Of course! You must have been, let me see, a little thing of almost two. I wanted to come and fetch you. But your grandfather wouldn't let me. I've often wondered why. He stayed with friends in Harley Street, and it was they who got a nurse for you. She traveled north when he brought you back here to me." Lady Mennock sat down on one side of the bed, struggled with memories for a moment, then turned with a rueful smile. "Funny timid little thing you were then. So like your poor mother, just at that stage. You were a great consolation to both of us, I don't know what we should have done without you!"

Margaret caught Lady Mennock's hand. She was touched and excited by this picture. It had, after all, been no mere cold curiosity that had prompted her to encourage these confidences. Was it not the story of her own parents and indeed her very young self that she was now hearing for the first time? And there was so much more that she wanted to know of these young unfortunates. Their way of life. Their relationship, one with the other. And her mother? "Were my parents staying with my mother's relatives in London, Granny?"

Lady Mennock shook her head slowly. "No. They weren't. Or at least if they were, we knew nothing about that. Certainly, your grandfather never saw them."

"Grandmother, who *was* my mother? What kind of person was she? Where did she come from? Don't you think it's time I was told these things?"

Lady Mennock withdrew her hand, stood up and turned. "Yes. I daresay it is," she said earnestly. "Your mother, Margaret, was—well, we never quite knew what she was. She was pretty and slight. You're built very like her. And she had gentle, but—what shall I say?—oddly elusive ways. She never quite answered the questions we asked her. I think she belonged to people connected with entertainment in some way. Dancing places or pantomimes—I don't know. She was a beautiful dancer, they say. So was your father. They danced wonderfully together, I've heard. Don't tell your grandfather, but someone once told me that they were seen giving performances together. In a dance hall in Blackpool, I think it was."

"Would you say my mother captured my father, guessing he was the son of a wealthy man?"

Lady Mennock shook her head. "No. You would never have thought that of her if you had known her, Margaret. Grace was a vague, starry little thing with a low, gentle voice. Never quite in the present, never quite attending to what was being said to her. No. I don't believe she could have thought of anything so—so definite."

"You make her sound simple-minded, Granny."

"She may have been."

"Or characterless?"

"Not quite. Your grandfather and I felt that the poor child did what she could with your father. No. There was a sweetness about Grace. Of course the marriage was unfortunate. But if they had only settled down beside us, I could have come to like her, I think."

Margaret felt touched. Did the qualities of sweetness ascribed to this girl begin and end in her grandmother's warm, impetuous charity? "But how did my mother and father come to meet each other? Where were they married?"

III

"In Scarborough it was."

"Scarborough? But why Scarborough?"

Lady Mennock merely sighed and shook her head. "You may well ask, Margaret. They never quite told us. We came to the conclusion she was giving some kind of summer performances there when your father came to know her. You see, we had lost him for a time and—"

"But, darling! How could you *lose* him?"

"We didn't always know where your father was. He used to worry us to death. He would simply go off without saying where he was going or when. It wasn't always possible to trace him at once. Sometimes people would tell us they had seen him; sometimes he was forced to give an address when he had no money; sometimes he simply reappeared."

Margaret looked up at her grandmother. There was nothing she could find to say. Was it possible that these two young people whose story she was engaged in writing, this James and Charlotte Mennock who had stood so firm—was it possible, that they could have become the parents of such a weakling? And was it possible that this weakling could have been her own father?

But her grandmother was going on. "Well, this time your father appeared, bringing your mother with him. And that's really all we know about that to this day—or all I know. I've sometimes wondered if your grandfather knew other things about his son, things he felt he couldn't tell me."

"But how strange of them simply to say nothing!"

"Oh, it wasn't that they didn't talk! They told us all kinds of things. But they left us in a mist."

"Untruthful?"

"Your grandfather insisted it wasn't quite that. Or at any rate that they didn't know what truth meant. I don't know, Margaret. I really can't tell you."

"Did they stay with you at that time, Granny?"

"For some weeks. That was all. Your grandfather arranged for your father to go into an office in town. I think he went for a week or two. We arranged to rent a small flat for them, and I was trying to interest Grace in furniture and showing her what nice things she could have in her own little home. But—but it was all no use. One day they—they just disappeared. You see they—"

"Granny! I've distressed you by asking about these things! Don't try to say any more!"

But she seemed determined to finish now. She wiped her eyes and went on: "After a time we found out they were dancing in some kind of musical play. I don't know what. One that traveled about, but didn't seem to travel to anywhere of importance. Still, your grandfather said that at least it was work of a sort and we had better leave them to it. But they didn't seem to be needed for long. After that they said they had to stay in London to get engagements."

"And did they get them?"

"Sometimes. Not very often. Anyway, your grandfather seemed forever to be getting desperate letters telling him what would happen if he didn't send help at once."

"Money?"

Lady Mennock nodded. "But when we heard you were coming, your grandfather put down his foot. He went up to London and brought them both back home. We felt Grace must be looked after. The baby had to be given its chance."

"I've read the entry for the day of my birth in Grandfather's diary."

"We thought your birth might help to settle them down, Margaret. But off they went again, taking you with them. That was the worst of all! I kept wondering what was happening to you and if you were being properly looked after. I had offered to keep you, of course. In fact I became quite desperate to keep you!"

"Granny!"

Charlotte Mennock's tears came freely now. "I went to my own mother about it. But she only scolded me and said that no woman, not even a grandmother, had any right to claim another woman's child!"

Margaret forced a smile. "Well never mind, darling! You got me in the end."

"I got you." Lady Mennock sought to impose calm upon herself. She crossed to Margaret's window and stood looking out for a time. When she turned to speak again her voice was once more even. "Yes. I got you, Margaret. But at a high cost. And yet, God forgive me, I've sometimes felt it was a cost that was better to be paid. You see, it was as though—what shall I say?—as though the thing inside people that keeps them standing upright had been left out of my poor son. In his last years he kept us in constant fear. Fear that he might do something very serious; something that— Well, anyhow, he didn't. Do you know, Margaret, I sometimes tell myself that your father's death was sent to protect him from himself. Do you think it's sinful to tell myself any such thing?"

"Not if you believe it, Granny." It was a strange point of view, perhaps. But why not allow her innocence this reassurance?

Lady Mennock crossed again to the bedside. "Yes. I got you and I've existed for you ever since."

"Darling! Haven't you existed for Grandfather too, a little?"

A smile began to hover. "Well, perhaps. When he wasn't too busy —or cross!"

IV

Doctor Joseph Struan was late. And, as he was keeping Mrs. Raymond waiting, for once his lateness really worried him. But since it was her grandfather who had kept him, there had been nothing for it but to remain until Sir James had seen fit to let him go. Besides the interview was of the first importance containing, as it did, a proposal that must be weighed and pondered and have its every facet examined.

The paragon had arranged to meet Margaret for lunch at one. It was already quarter past as he left his car at the park nearest to their usual restaurant and began impatiently to shoulder his way among the mob on the crowded pavement.

This Canadian professorship that Sir James had as good as offered him some minutes since? Well, yes. His life, he supposed, was dedicated to academic medicine. Before he had stepped into the Glasgow plane in London last September and taken his place beside Sir James's granddaughter, he could have said with his hand on his heart that his career was the whole of his life. His parents were dead. And he had no ties. He had been content to give his work all his energy, all his emotion.

Deep in thought, the paragon did not notice that he had come to a street crossing and stepped off the pavement to collide with a taxi that was nosing its way round the corner. In language enriched by Glasgow invective the driver requested him to look where he was going. Joe Struan rubbed an injured leg, struck mud from his overcoat and pressed on.

Would Mrs. Raymond, Margaret, as now he had been told to call her, still be waiting for him? Or would she have decided that he had no right to keep her waiting and have gone away? And this Canadian business? He wanted very specially to know what she thought about it. Though he had not yet had time fully to consider Sir James's proposal, the paragon had already decided that Canada would be a flat, unprofitable place if it did not contain a slim young woman with pale skin and a crop of dark-red hair. Not that he had ever got within miles of suggesting to her that she might remedy the flatness and lack of profit in Canada or anywhere else. But now, as he saw it, these miles would have to be made to shrink somehow before he felt in the least like—

"I'm sorry!" This time he had collided with a large wooden packing case which was being carried carefully from a van across the pavement into a furniture shop by two stalwarts in dirty white aprons. For a moment they tottered, seeking to save the case and themselves from crashing to the ground; then they set it down, turned to the young man's large receding back, and in language even more rich than the language of the taximan likewise requested him to look where he was going.

Margaret had by now shown him all she had so far written of her grandparents' story. Passionately interested in everything that concerned the Mennocks, Joe had become as obsessed with what she was doing as she herself was. They were forever discussing moves and motives. To the paragon, this retracing of the steps which brought together these two people who stood so high in his veneration, had chimed perfectly with his mood this winter. A mood of happiness hitherto unknown to a lonely young man.

Many times, down there in Miss McQueen's basement, he had raised his eyes to watch Margaret typing at her table; holding an old letter to the light; triumphantly scribbling a note in order to pin down a clue.

To the young doctor, her natural elegance, her movements, her frail build—qualities inherited, though he could not know this, from the tragic little showgirl who had been her mother—had given her an unreality, making him feel that his work companion was made of some different, more precious clay. And she had, as they had come better to know each other, taken to turning round, now and then, radiant at some find. "Joe, just listen! What would you say young James was feeling when he wrote this?" It wasn't fair. Yet how could she know that her presence so disturbed him?

A last street crossing. A final collision with the snorting nose of a drayhorse as it labored up the hill and the paragon had reached port; meeting, as he passed into the warmth of their restaurant, an atmosphere redolent of Mediterranean herbs and respectful, foreign greetings.

She called to him as he came upstairs into the busy lunch room.

For a moment he stood, large and bewildered, peering about him until he had caught her in the circle of his restricted vision, then he came forward. "Good—good morning. I'm very late. I—I thought you might have gone away."

"Oh? Why?"

"Well—I—you might have thought I wasn't coming."

She laughed at this in a way that made him wonder if there were echoes of mockery. "I'm a doctor's granddaughter. I should know by now that doctors can be kept late." And then, as his only reply was uncertainty and silence: "Go and take off your coat, Joe. I'm starving with hunger."

The paragon's teeth gleamed for a moment in a pleased, vague smile as he turned away to hang it up.

V

Thus they had become good friends, this brilliant, strangely boyish

[174]

man and this girl whose few adult years had been fraught with joy and sorrow, fraught with happenings which had developed her sympathy and quickened her understanding. She had broken down the barrier of his paralyzing shyness, and having done this had found what lay behind was worth her while.

There had been little difficulty in finding things to talk about at these lunchtime meetings. Most of them, indeed, had become friendly wrangles; Margaret, relying upon her skirmishing intuitions to outwit the heavy artillery of Joe's arguments; each of them pursuing the game with an amused concentration that left food cold on plates and waiters impatient and wondering why these two bothered to meet each other merely to argue. It was the age-old battle of sex, of course, though neither of these clever young people saw this.

But today neither could strike fire from the other. Each sat nursing a separate preoccupation.

It was Margaret who first spoke of hers. "Joe," she began, "I've found out all about my father and mother. It's a wretched story. I can't get it out of my head."

"You've found out?"

The tone of his voice caused her to look up. "Yes. Poor Granny told me two days ago. Why are you so surprised?"

The paragon was afraid he was looking guilty. As a way of dissembling, he took off his glasses and began polishing them, fixing Margaret with a glazed, unfocused look. "Surprised? No. Why should I be?" And then, though he felt conscious of a telltale color rising, curiosity forced him to add: "You could have read it in Sir James's diaries."

"I promised Grandfather not to look at them until he gave me his permission; until he felt like telling me about my parents himself. But I saw no reason to stop Grandmother if she felt like telling me. Would you?"

"No." Joe heaved a sigh of relief—he was not quite sure why—and replaced the spectacles upon his square face. So she had not been searching for the diary that Sir James was anxious she should not see.

"When you've got it, Joe, bring it to me." Despite his injured hand he had brought the diary to Sir James.

Now Margaret was talking. Telling him what she knew of her parents. But he did not give her all his attention. His thoughts had gone back.

He had found the diary and brought it to the old man who had turned to the entry then closed it at once. "That's the one, Joe. Thanks for bringing it. Have you looked at it?" "Oh, no, sir! I didn't think I had the right to do that." "Good boy! My son Sandy and his wife reached the end on the last day of October 1930. You can read it. You may as well know the truth." "I'm not sure that I want to, sir." "Very well, Joe. Please yourself." And he had taken it and locked it in a drawer of his desk. But the words "reached the end" had nagged at Joe's curiosity. What had the old man meant? There had been moments when he regretted he had not read what Sir James had written.

The waiter came to set coffee before them. Time was going on.

"I've sometimes wondered," Margaret was now concluding, "how my grandparents have been able to go on being so—I can only call it young. You must know what I mean."

He merely nodded, blinking and turning the stem of his wineglass.

"But people do seem to get over loss, Joe. Even a bad one, don't you think?"

"You can answer that better than I can, Margaret."

Her color rose. "I wasn't thinking of myself just now." She halted, then went on: "Yes. I daresay. I've been happier this winter than I ever expected to be again. Thanks to—" she stopped to laugh a little, "thanks to the fact that I had quite forgotten to wonder whether I was happy or not!"

And it may be that the paragon, being foolishly in love, read meanings into these words, meanings she had in no way intended.

VI

At all events, he now felt he must speak of her grandfather's proposal to know how she would take it. "I—I don't think I told you I was with Sir James this morning."

"Oh? Were you?" Why this embarrassment? Why the husky throat?

"He was making me an offer."

"An offer, Joe?"

"Or at any rate he was passing on an offer."

"Well?" What was wrong with the man?

"It—it was the offer of a professorship in Canada."

Margaret smiled. "Shall I tell you a secret?"

He nodded.

"Grandfather told me about this—oh—it must have been weeks ago. He asked me if I thought you were the right man for the job."

The paragon's embarrassment became visibly painful. "And—what did you say?"

"What *could* I say? How could I be expected to know? I told Grandfather that if you were as brilliant as he always claimed you were then a professorship somewhere seemed to be the obvious thing for you. Don't you think it is?"

"I—I wish I knew." He had not expected this bright impersonality.

"I expect you'll decide to go," her voice went on gaily. "You've no one here at home now. Have you?"

He drew out his handkerchief and wiped his brow. "I—don't want to leave Glasgow."

"Oh? Why?"

This was terrible! He had not expected these tones of crisp, cool interest. Some sign, some betraying emotion, was what he had hoped for, was all he needed meantime; all his extreme shyness was ready for. But now, having got thus far, "I must— Margaret, I've—"

But the tones that now interposed were firm. "I wish I could advise you about this, Joe. If Donald, my husband, had been alive, he could have told you about life in Eastern Canada. He was there for a short time on a special reporting job during the war." She was looking at her watch. "Is it really so late? I had no idea. Well, perhaps, if you wouldn't mind— You'll be up at Woodside Terrace soon, won't you?"

When she had gone, the inevitable glasses came off his nose yet once again and he sat, foolish and flushed, polishing them for a long time. No. He would, it seemed, have to do better than that.

CHAPTER SIXTEEN

I

Having heard Peggy and Davie read what she called "their daily portion," Constance did not go back to her stepson who was still at breakfast.

"While you and Davie are having your cup of tea, Peggy," she said, "I'll just go out to the meat safe and take a peep at the leftovers. Just to see how you and I can manage to eke things out." She smiled here, adding: "*Waste not, want not,* David; that's the motto of all good housekeepers, isn't it, Peggy?"

But Peggy, already heading for the breakfast teapot, was disappearing through the kitchen doorway with what might, or might not, have been taken as a flounce. Waste there assuredly never was in this house. And perhaps not want either, exactly. But there were such things as quantities too nicely measured. There were times too when cupboards could be relocked with a promptitude that implied suspicion, if not accusation. As if a lassie ever thought of touching anything that wasna her own!

Constance unlocked the safe, looked round it and assured herself that the shreds of meat and suet adhering to sundry bones would, when scraped off and minced, be enough—with a generous covering of potato—to make a delicious shepherd's pie for the midday meal. Then she shut and locked the door again. She would give these bones to Peggy presently.

Next she sighed, stood still for a moment, then told herself she ought to have a look at what David had done, or left undone, in the vegetable garden here at the back of Gowan Bank. But she was merely giving herself a pretext. She was worried about her stepson and she wanted to walk in the fresh air and think.

It was a warm morning of promise in early March. The kind of morning that should come at the end of this unstable month and not at its beginning. New-turned earth looked dark and fecund. The grass, no longer winter-sodden, was dew-crisp and green. Canes and bushes showed signs of sprouting. A flock of starlings, settled in a row along a rooftop, chattered and preened themselves, black, against the brightness of the sky. Persistent cock crowing came from the far distance, just distinguishable—when the noise of the starlings would allow it—above the low, ever present droning of the cotton mills.

She took her way up the incline of the narrow drive which ran up on one side of the modest kitchen garden and ended at the pony's stable and harness room, there against the hill. Her brows, surmounted still by curl and fringe, were contracted by anxiety. She went slowly, a black figure, thin and troubled. Her hands clasped in front of her, her eyes upon the ground.

What was it that was wrong with Bruce? Why these ill manners? This sudden snapping at her in a way she would never have allowed his little father to do? Why should she put up with it?

For a moment Constance stood still, drew her handkerchief from her belt, dabbed her eyes and decided to indulge in self-pity. But at once she knew this to be a false indulgence. She put away her handkerchief, replaced her eye clips and continued upwards. No. It wasn't Bruce's impatient words that had distressed her. In these last months, she had grown too fond of Peter Mennock's son to be really distressed by such things as that. But in these days he seemed so unhappy; so unhappy that he was getting ill. Yet he would say nothing and she dare not ask, dare do nothing to help him.

He had snapped at her fretfully this morning. On hearing the postman's step, she had risen from breakfast and gone to the front door. At this moment Bruce had come downstairs.

"Oh, there you are, Bruce. Let me see. These seem to be for you."

"That's right, Mother. Have a good look at them. Be sure you know where all my letters come from!"

At once she had given them all into his hand. "Bruce! Are you accusing me of prying?"

Without a word he had taken them, turned from her and gone in to breakfast.

Arrived at the top of the garden, Constance crossed to an old seat placed against the stable wall. Deciding it looked dry, she sat down for a moment in the sunshine.

No, this wasn't Bruce. Not even the Bruce she had known as an adolescent. Certainly not the responsible young man who had stepped in, soberly and without fuss, at the time of his father's death. What had changed him? When had this strange behavior begun to show itself? Constance reflected. Some weeks ago? Since the beginning of the year? He had suddenly announced one morning in January that business required him in Glasgow. On his return that afternoon he had as usual told her nothing. But he had seemed on edge and had refused to eat his evening meal.

Why should he always repulse her anxious questions? Why couldn't he tell her what was wrong? Constance could only sigh and sit unhappily looking about her. Yes. It was about then that his dark moods had begun.

Davie had come out at the back door of the house, closing it with a bang. She watched him as he sauntered up towards her. Responding to the sunshine, to the promise in the air, he had stuck his thumbs into the armholes of his waistcoat and was whistling tunelessly.

"Lovely morning, isn't it, David? Quite like spring," Constance called, bestowing upon him a smile that was at once birdlike and regal.

Feeling somehow reproved, the stable boy started. He had not noticed his mistress sitting up there. "Yes, mum." Respectfully he removed his thumbs, dropped his casual amble and made to walk past her with guilty speed.

"Is the doctor going out in the trap this morning?" Constance asked genially.

"Aye. That's right, mum. He's just been askin' me to pit in the pauny." Davie disappeared into the building behind her.

II

Again the back door banged and she raised her eyes to see her stepson advancing hat in hand. Why was he coming up to the stable? Usually, of a morning, Bruce allowed David to take the trap to the front gate.

Now, as he approached, Constance was dismayed to see his face was dark with trouble. On catching sight of her, however, he seemed to take hold of himself. Was it to her that he was coming?

"Oh, you're there, Mother? Peggy said you were out here somewhere."

She smiled towards him encouragingly. "Having a look at the garden, Bruce. Enjoying this sudden sunshine." Then, as he stood hovering uncertainly, she moved to make room. "Do sit down for a moment. Just to feel how warm it is already."

James placed his large, disconsolate frame beside her. Then bent forward, crouched and sulky, dangling his hat between his knees.

His stepmother watched him, glad that he had come to sit beside her, yet still afraid to speak lest what she said be wrong.

Presently he straightened himself, put his hat on the seat beside him and looked at her. "I'm sorry about this morning, Mother. I want to apologize."

"Apologize, Bruce? For what?"

"For how I behaved about the letters."

"Oh, that? My dear boy, I had forgotten all about it!" His words touched Constance, justifying her, she felt, in this lie of forgiveness. "Surely we understand each other very well by this time!"

"Very good of you to put up with me, Mother." James tossed back a lock of hair and looked about him, the sunshine causing him to contract the features of his pale face. "I'm turning into a bad-tempered devil, that's what's wrong with me."

"You're strained, dear. Things have got on your nerves. Can't you get someone to take your place for a fortnight?"

"If anybody needs a holiday it's you, Mother." James put forth a long leg and began to kick one heel into the green turf in front of him. When he spoke again he spoke low and, as it seemed, to himself. "There are worse things in this world than just plain work."

She was neither quick nor clever but her feelings told her that now, for the first time in their lives perhaps, her stepson was poised, awaiting her encouragement, seeking the solace of her confidence. For a moment she sat uncertain and afraid. She was so bad at this. And yet so anxious to help him. What must she say to open up the way? But she must try! "It's not for me to ask, of course, Bruce, but you seem to me to have been getting more and more strained ever since you went to Glasgow in—when was it— January?"

"January?" He looked at her, then turned away and began once more to kick the turf. "I went to see Professor Mackinnon Gailes in January," he said.

"Professor—? You've never told me you were on visiting terms, Bruce! At least—"

"Well I'm not on 'visiting terms' now, Mother." Then, as she said nothing: "Would you like to read a letter?"

"If you want me to read it, Bruce."

"I got that this morning." James had taken an envelope from his pocket. "That's what the strain's about, Mother, if you would like to know."

Primly she drew out the letter, unfolded it, and adjusted her eye clips. It was written, this time, in a hand she did not recognize.

DEAR DOCTOR MENNOCK,

Today I came upon a number of letters which appear to have been written by you to my daughter since our interview in January. We told you then that we considered your conduct towards her dishonorable and begged you to leave her alone.

Since your continued importuning of her is making her ill and unhappy, we must ask you to distress her no more.

Meanwhile my husband and I are considering what further steps had better be taken.

Sincerely,
EDITH MACKINNON GAILES

"Bruce!" Constance gave the letter back to him. "What *is* this? I didn't know you were writing to any young lady! Is this her mother?"

"That's her mother."

"But— Oh, I wish you had told me about this sooner!"

The reply to this was a mere sulky kicking of the turf.

"Bruce, I must know more! What can I say to help you if you won't tell me about it?"

For a moment James appeared to hesitate, then he took a second letter from his pocketbook. "You had better read this as well, Mother." He had risen from the bench and had now begun to pace back and forth in front of her.

III

The letter bore a January date.

MY OWN DARLING JAMES,

When I got back for lunch today I was told you had been here and that I had missed you. Can I ever forgive myself? Oh I can't bear the thought of it! What *did* Mother and Father say to you? And what *did* you say to them? Now they are plunged in such impenetrable gloom, that they will tell me next to nothing. Very kind, and tragic, and all that sort of thing. But I wish they would stop this poor-erring-child nonsense, and really tell me what everybody said to everybody else! They insist that nothing really *was* said. Yet at the same time they also insist—or at least Mother does—that your behavior showed once and for all that you were no fit person ever to be a son-in-law of theirs.

Of course I burst into tears and told them I knew you far better than they did; and that you were the best and cleverest person in the world; and that I was going to marry you whether they thought you fit or not fit! At which they produced more gentleness and reason; and said that I couldn't possibly judge people at my age; and that it was their duty as my parents to protect me from myself. Also that I would be sure to regret marrying you the moment I had done it!

Oh, my darling, write at once and tell me I shall never do that! That, whatever happens, I shall always be safe with you!

I find, too, that they told you flatly that they wanted nothing more to do with you, whereupon you banged out of the house in a rage. And quite right too! But how dreadful! And how utterly miserable for me! I turn hot and cold with shame for my parents every time I think of it!

But, dearest love, what are we going to do? I feel as though we were standing together before a blank wall! And I feel this is dreadfully unfair to you with all your other troubles! Oh I *must* see you and talk to you! The very first moment we can! Though meeting won't be easy now. Not that I am likely to be locked up or anything, but Mother is bound to keep an eye on my movements for a time at least. They have not questioned me about letters. Father thinks these kind of questions vulgar, thank goodness! So you can safely write. Address as usual.

Oh, how I hate all this! This misery for you, and this misery for me! Yes, and this misery for my poor, misguided parents! As you know, darling, I love them dearly. But then, I love you more and I can't change myself, can I? So there's nothing to be done, is there? Oh, why won't they try to understand? Why won't they see that now I am grown up and entitled to have grown-up feelings? Still, as I keep telling myself, they mean well, I daresay.

I hope you got my telegram and that it helped to stiffen you! Write to me at once if you haven't done so already. I *must* know what you feel.

You have all my love, my very dearest. That is, if you want it after what happened this morning! No. Whether you want it or not! But what can we do, James? What can we *do*?

Your wife-to-be, whatever anybody else likes to think,

CHARLOTTE

P.S. I have just been thinking. Do you remember I wrote you from Lausanne once about a German girl who had eloped with an Italian student? The man turned out to have no proper principles, we heard later. He didn't even marry her, and she was brought to *shame* and *disaster,* poor soul! But I am certain there is nothing wrong with your principles, James. And I *know* mine are very *firm*. But we shan't really have to elope, shall we?   C.

Constance looked up, bewildered. What was she to make of this girl's strange letter? This revelation of a love affair between this professor's daughter and her stepson? An affair she had never, despite her interest in handwriting, really suspected? She looked across at his back as now he moved away from her, at his bent shoulders, at his jacket raised and rumpled behind by the hands thrust deep into his pockets, at his restless, unhappy pacing.

Oh, why wasn't his father here to help him? She had never felt so near to her husband's son! Never come so near to yearning over him! Breaking reserve he had handed her this love letter in his desperation; seeking sympathy from someone; even from her unsure, fumbling self! What could she, the ineffective creature who was Constance Mennock, possibly find to say to this young man in his trouble?

But now indignation flooded her biased, loyal heart. Who did this professor and his wife think they were, that they should imagine Peter Mennock's son not fit to marry their daughter? Whom better would they find? Whom more serious? Whom more trustworthy? More promising? Couldn't this Glasgow professor find out what they were saying about this new-fledged Glasgow doctor?

And the girl herself? What kind of creature was this Charlotte Gailes who was obsessing James, bringing him to the breaking point? A petted minx? Not quite. No. It didn't seem to be the girl's fault. This letter was all distress and indignation.

And yet its tone puzzled Constance. Was it merely that the writer had a way of overdramatizing everything? Irresponsible? Unfolding the sheets once again and glancing through them, Constance could not find them so. No, not irresponsible. Except that part about elopement in the postscript. But of course Miss Gailes hadn't meant that.

"Well, Mother?" There was a rueful smile on James's face as she looked up to find him standing over her.

"Bruce! I had no idea this was going on!"

"Well, you know now."

"But didn't anybody else?"

"We were promised to one another in the Lyndochs' house last July."

Constance drew herself up and let her eyebrows arch themselves into the beginnings of resentment. "Bertha might at least have told me," she said.

"Aunt Bertha advised us to keep quiet until everything was fair and square with Charlotte's father and mother." Here James stopped, looked aside angrily, then turned back to repeat the words: "Fair and square!" with contempt.

Constance was filled with curiosity. She had all kinds of hows and whys to put to him. But first she must find how things stood now. "But if all this happened in the middle of January, what has happened since?"

"Not much. What *could* happen? We write letters every day. You'll have noticed some of them." Constance chose to ignore this.

"I've met her once. It wasna easy to arrange. They keep a tight grip on her. Oh I don't know—I'm beginning to think I've just about reached—"

"Reached what, dear?"

"The end."

"I don't understand, Bruce."

"No more do I."

Constance looked up at him nervously: "Bruce! It frightens me to hear you talking like that! Oh! These horrible people are making you ill!"

James was astonished at the sight of tears. It had never occurred to him that his stepmother might actually be fond of him. "It's all right, Mother. Never you heed."

"It would serve them right if you *did* run away!" Constance said indignantly, wiping her eyes.

"Charlotte didna mean that, Mother. She sometimes writes things she doesna mean, just because, well, because they've come into her head."

But now, since Davie had appeared with the pony and trap, Constance quite suddenly assumed her public countenance; a habit that

[185]

had ever infuriated her husband and her stepson. She drew herself up regally and smiled. "There's David, dear. I really mustn't keep you from work any longer." Then, raising her voice to shrill brightness, she added: "I'm sure the sun's going to keep out all morning, David! You'll be able to make up for lost time in the garden, won't you?"

IV

"I'm beginning to think I've just about reached the end!"

He had said this in a way that alarmed his stepmother and she had asked him what he meant. He could not tell her because he could not tell himself. "Just about reached the end!"

In the two days that followed, these words hung unhappily in his overcharged heart. What end? Going about his work, sitting at the meals he could scarcely touch, lying sleepless in bed, James kept asking himself this question—and muttering to himself as often as he asked it: "Some kind of end, anyway!"

The letter from Edith Gailes had stretched his taut senses still further; senses already stretched to their limit between pride, hotly and bitterly wounded by Charlotte's parents, and this passion for their daughter that had come upon him unawares and would not let him go.

Some kind of end must come soon, he told himself. This torment must not be allowed to last. Yet what must he do to put a stop to it? James did not know.

And then, after these two days, Charlotte's telegram came. He was beginning a morning round in the village when he met the boy from the post office and took it from him. Guessing whence it came, he tore it open, fumbling in his excitement. For once the fingers of James Mennock were ill-controlled and clumsy.

COME AT ONCE AT HOME ALONE ALL TODAY MUST SEE YOU THEY ARE TAKING ME AWAY.

He crushed the telegram into his pocket, mumbled: "No answer," and swung round on his heel. As he walked back to Gowan Bank he told himself the end had come. What end he still did not know. But now he knew that it was here.

"Bruce! Why have you come back? Are you ill?" At the sight of him, Constance, all too ready to be concerned, felt cold with apprehension.

[186]

"Never heed about me. I'm all right. I've had a wire from Charlotte Gailes! I've got to see her today! There's a train in half an hour."

"When do you expect to be home, dear?"

"I've no idea."

She heard him noisily opening and shutting drawers in his room upstairs. What was he doing? Was he taking out clothes? And what about his patients? What was happening about anything?

She met him as he ran downstairs again, carrying a packed hand-bag. "Bruce, are you going to be away all night?"

"I canna tell you, Mother. I havena thought."

"You haven't—! Then why—? Bruce, what am I to do if people come? Bruce you *must* tell me! I must know what to do!"

There were other doctors not far away, he said, as he struggled into his overcoat. And Davie had the pony trap to help fetch and carry. At the door he turned. "Do what you think best, Mother."

"Bruce, what are you going to do? Is this wise?"

"This morning I canna tell what's wise and what's not wise, Mother. But something's got to happen now!" With that he left her. But he had not reached the front gate before he heard her calling after him: "Bruce! Bruce! What about money? Have you got any? Look, dear; there are some pounds in my housekeeping box."

"Thank heaven you reminded me, Mother. I'll call at the bank."

But in the midmorning train that bore him to Glasgow, James was forced to sit still and examine his feelings; to ask himself what, indeed, he meant to do. The thought of again seeing Charlotte and the knowledge that now he must act promptly, breaking in upon hopelessness and dejection, had brought a mood of strange exhilaration. A quickening and renewing of his will. Frustration was coming to an end. But how? What were his instincts telling him to do? He looked at the bag he had thrown into the rack opposite. Why had he bothered with that? To be able to stay overnight if need be? Where? In Glasgow?

In that letter he had shown to his stepmother Charlotte had written of elopement. Well? What of it? If there were no other way? Had Charlotte's irresponsibility tossed the seed into his mind? And was it germinating? Would he, if it proved possible, elope with Charlotte now?

In his corner seat, James looked at the Ayrshire fields as they fled past the window. At the herds of grazing cattle. At the red, new-plowed earth. From these he turned to look at his fellow passengers;

a fussed young woman with two complaining little children she was seeking to placate with biscuits. But though his eyes recorded these things, his mind could not take them in.

No. Not elope. Not if eloping meant a vulgar seduction. If he had to break her parents' unreason by taking her from them, then he would marry her at once.

James held Charlotte on a pedestral. This young girl who had surprised his senses must be protected from the breath of scandal before he took her to him. Did she not trust him utterly? A trust that had begun with the first moment of their first meeting? And was not this trust among the strongest of the chains that bound him to her?

But how could this be brought about? James put his brow against the coldness of his window and went on staring at the flying fields and hedges, searching his mind with diligence.

A minister? A minister of religion could do it, surely? Not the Kinaldie parish minister, nor yet the minister of the professor's church in Glasgow. He could not ask either of these for help. Their marriage must, James argued, confusing religion with the law, take place at once and secretly before it could be stopped. Had it not been done for others? Why not for Charlotte and himself? But who would do this for them?

The train was slowing down to cross the river Clyde, jangling and shifting over the switches as it swung round into St. Enoch's Station, before Hector Duart came into James's mind.

The face of a sick young man on a hospital pillow. A serious operation. The face wax-white and suffering as presently they had all of them fought to keep life in those dark, searching eyes. The slow first stages while victory hung uncertain, while every day downstairs a strained young woman must be given falsely cheerful news. The news no longer false. The woman's first permitted visit, bringing their young child with her. Joy—and health returning faster. A long-legged doctor, red-haired and disputatious, who stopped by the bed to contradict outrageously the young minister's fixed opinions of the universe. Alert to stimulate his returning spirit. Alert neither to weary nor exhaust. A friendship formed between a man of twenty-four and a man of thirty, that had perhaps meant more to the Reverend Hector Duart of the village of West Hyde, Dumfriesshire, than to the houseman to whom he believed himself to owe his life.

"Owe your life to me, Mr. Duart? What about owing it to all the others?" James had protested as he gave him his hand at the door of the cab which the young woman had at last brought to carry her husband back to his manse and normality. But, as often with convalescents, Hector Duart had found emotion too near the surface to allow him to argue. He had merely stood rather foolishly holding James's hand until his wife, brisk and plump and once again self-confident, had exclaimed: "Come away inside, Hector, and don't keep the doctor from his work! He knows fine what we both think about him! Did you ask him to come and see us, when I told you? Or did you forget as usual?"

"You'll come, won't you, Doctor Mennock?"

"I'll come when I can, Mr. Duart."

But there had been so much since then. Only a few letters had passed between them and the parish minister of West Hyde had receded to the back of James's mind. But just now, to his friend's overwhelming relief, the Reverend Mr. Duart was there once again in the forefront.

The train came to a standstill beneath the smoky dome of St. Enoch's Station. James stood up and took down his bag. Next, quite impersonally and without thought, he took down the woman's parcels handing these, together with the two biscuit-covered children, out to her as she stood to receive them on the platform. Then, jumping down himself and pushing his way among the other passengers, he set out at a half-run down the platform. He was pleased he had remembered their friendship. If Charlotte and he should decide to turn and run, Hector Duart was their man.

CHAPTER SEVENTEEN

I

If Charlotte and he should decide to turn and run? Was not his own decision already taken? But would Charlotte consent to it? Suppose that she began by refusing? How far would it be right for him to press her? Yet had she not sent for him? Was she not, little as she had been able to see him in these last weeks, in terror of being taken further from him?

Hopes, fears, scruples, questions, strove with each other as James made his way westwards towards the university, confusion and uncertainty mounting as he neared his destination.

And yet in a moment, when he had bounded up the professor's front steps and the door had been opened without his ringing to reveal Charlotte standing there in front of him, confusion and uncertainty lifted from James's mind like a curtain, giving place to decision and a strange sense of relief.

"Come in, James. I've been watching for you. Father and Mother had to go to a wedding in Edinburgh. They won't be back until late."

She looked frail and very young and her eyes were ringed with shadows as though she had not slept. Yet these weeks, it now seemed to him, had given her a new firmness.

But it was a firmness that melted when he had followed her into the professor's library and the door was shut behind them. In a moment she was in his arms weeping her heart out, while he carried her to a chair, fondling her and talking nonsense as though she were a child, seeking to give her comfort. And seeking, too, to find comfort for himself; to feed the hunger of those days that lay behind him.

At last, when the storm had raged itself to a finish, Charlotte freed herself from his arms and turned to look at him. Meeting his eyes, examining his face with the unassuageable curiosity of young love. At last she spoke. "James, this can't go on."

"No."

"It's been making you ill. It's been making me ill too." And as her voice was in danger of becoming drowned again, Charlotte, seeking for control, drew herself away from him and stood up.

"Where do they say they are going to take you?"

"To Italy. Rome. Only for about a month, they say. But they mean to find somewhere to leave me."

"Like enough."

"But I *know*, James! I was with Mother when she was asking about the tickets. She's buying them to Rome only. She said we could see about getting home when once we had got there and knew what our arrangements were to be. Anyway, we can't risk it. At least—I don't want to, do you?"

"No."

"But James, what are we to do?"

He was lying back in her father's fireside chair, searching the face, the aspect of this young girl without whom life would become for him a mere treadmill. Now, with a Scotsman's burning interest in his conscience, he was searching his heart, sternly and for the last time, before he asked his question.

His somber look kept her silent, waiting.

"Charlotte, will you come away with me?"

"Now, James? Today?"

"When else could we go?"

"No. We couldn't go at any other time."

She had answered this merely to give herself time, James saw. Her lip was trembling and she was shaken. But he did not move, did not rise from his chair to confuse or persuade her with caresses. She must answer this for herself.

"But who would marry us?"

"I have a friend, a minister near Dumfries, who would marry us tonight."

Tears had again begun to make their way down her cheeks. "I love my parents, James."

"I know. But your parents have made it— Charlotte, it's either them or me!"

Her next words were spoken in a dazed whisper of desperation. "Yes. They have, haven't they?" For a little time longer she stood letting her tears flow quietly; then of a sudden she gave way, throwing herself down wild and weeping on the hearthrug in front of him, pushing herself between his knees, and thrusting her arms about his waist. "James! James, take me away! Take me with you! You must take me with you!"

He could feel the pounding of his own heart as he sat there, her prisoner, stroking the head that lay against him and waiting until this storm too was ended. But at last he set his hands upon her shoulders, pushed her gently from him; rising himself, he raised her to her feet. "Go and put some things in a bag, and we'll get away." He spoke quietly, seeking to impose calm—calm upon Charlotte and calm upon himself. "Is there anybody in the house that might try to stop us?"

She shook her head.

"Very well. In less than half an hour I'll be here with a cab. Be ready, waiting. Whenever you see it, open the door and come." As she turned he caught her arm. "And no message left behind, Charlotte! Your folks will be told. They'll be sent word whenever we're safely married."

II

It was late afternoon when the train that brought James and Charlotte from Glasgow slowed down and stopped in the Scottish border town of Dumfries. It was darker than it should have been for clouds hung low and a fine rain was falling. But James was glad to find himself here; glad to be handing Charlotte from the railway carriage; glad of the noise and the lights in the station of this pleasant county town; glad that the long afternoon journey in a train that had stopped everywhere had come at last to an end.

It had been a difficult journey. Their purpose, indeed, stood fixed. But there had been more than ample time for first enthusiasms to cool; for questions again to take shape; for doubts about ways and procedures; doubts about what they now must do. It had on the whole been best, James decided, that he had not been left alone with Charlotte in the railway carriage; that chance had always replaced the people descending at country stations. He felt that it had been easier for Charlotte and indeed for himself too to be forced to keep countenance before these strangers. He had more than once surprised her attempting to brush aside a tear unnoticed; whereat his heart had jumped to his throat in trouble and tenderness. But he had been forced to pretend he did not see. Charlotte, he knew, was struggling to keep calm, and attempts at comfort must almost certainly have ended any calmness.

[192]

For some minutes they stood together on the wet platform. A long young man with the collar of his overcoat turned up, looking anxiously about him, a worn gladstone bag dangling from one hand, a rather better, much-traveled one plastered with the labels of foreign hotels, dangling from the other, and a tall, slender girl beside him, bravely looking about her too as she clung closely to his arm.

"He doesna seem to have got here," James said at length, referring to the Reverend Hector Duart to whom he had sent a telegram stating that he, James, was arriving that evening on particular and very important business, and begging Mr. Duart if possible to meet him at Dumfries.

"No, James. What do you think we should do?"

On the train journey James had considered this possibility. "There's only the one thing to be done. Take a cab and drive out to West Hyde Manse."

"What if they're not at home, James?"

"Aye, they'll be at home. What would the minister of the parish not be at home for?"

She followed him to the station entrance where they found a cab. "Is it far out to West Hyde?" James asked.

"Yer no expectin' me to drive ye away there!" the driver asked. "It'll be an 'oor onyway."

"We've got to get there tonight!" And then his embarrassment quite foolishly imagining the man was questioning Charlotte's respectability, James added: "We're going to the West Hyde Manse. The minister and his wife expect us. An hour's not long. And you'll be paid for it."

The creaking cab, with its interior smelling of horse, wet and trampled sheepskin rug and stale tobacco smoke, rattled its way out of the streets of Dumfries, into the rich farmlands of southern Scotland. During all of this long sodden drive in the waning half-light, James lay against the worn leather seat holding Charlotte in his arms. He was glad that she was content thus, that for most of the way she did not speak. There were times, indeed, when he wondered if she were asleep and hoped that it might be so.

Yet this left him alone with his own apprehensions. What if his reverend friend was not to be found as Charlotte had suggested? What if the windows of the manse were dark? What if Mrs. Duart should resent a young woman, unknown and unaccounted for except by a very young man, being thrust upon her? What if she should counsel her husband to do nothing? What if—? No. Why allow himself these questions? He was tired and overwrought. Let him think of the unhappy days, the weeks of misery and affront this day of determined purpose was putting behind him; let him remember the battle was now all but won and that this evening would complete his victory.

But when at length they came to West Hyde village and presently turned in beneath the dark shapes of the high bare trees in the manse grounds, James was much reassured to see its windows lighted and that, too, a horse and gig was being led away into the gloom. Now he could see the outline of a man halt, then turn round in the lighted doorway.

When the cab came to a standstill, the parish minister of West Hyde ran back down his front steps to open for them. "Doctor Mennock! I thought you would have got here by this time! We had your wire. Mrs. Duart is delighted! You will be staying the night? But I couldn't get to Dumfries. I had a funeral, and you see—" he stopped here, seeing another emerge from the darkness of the cab. "A young lady, Doctor? Not a Mrs. Mennock? We didna know!" He shook Charlotte by the hand.

James made an effort to go straight to the point, cabman's presence or no cabman's presence. "We're here to ask you to *make* her Mrs. Mennock, Mr. Duart."

"So you're to be married soon? And I'm to be asked to marry you? Mrs. Duart will be pleased about that now! Neither of us have forgotten what you did for me, you know, Doctor. It's a thing I'll do with great pleasure! Great pleasure indeed!" Then, seeing that James seemed troubled and preoccupied as he turned to pay the cabman: "Well! Well! You come away inside with me, my dear. Mrs. Duart will be delighted to see you."

III

Mary Duart had just succeeded in putting her eighteen-month-old son to sleep in the large bedroom which she, her husband and the son in question occupied in the old, comfortable manse of West Hyde. While she waited with the child, she had several times gone next door to the guest room to see if the fire she had lit for Doctor Mennock's comfort had taken hold and was burning brightly. Now she heard the sound of hooves and wheels on the gravel outside,

[194]

then the voice of the man as he took charge of the manse gig; all of which sounds were familiar and which she rightly took to be the sounds of her husband's return.

She was glad of this. Glad that Hector should be here to welcome his friend, the doctor, and occupy him while she herself saw to things. But the sounds of arrival seemed to go on. Sounds unlike those her husband usually made when he was getting back from parish duties. A man's voice. Doctor Mennock's? Yes. These were the tones she remembered. She hoped he would stay now that she had done her best to prepare for him. A woman's? No. It couldn't be. It would be too bad if some, probably difficult, church member had arrived just at this point to take up Hector's time. For an instant she wondered why he was not shouting for her, as was his habit at such tangled moments, to descend to the hall and disentangle him; then she decided she had better go and see for herself. A last look at the sleeping child. The lamp turned low. The flicker of the fire casting shadows about the country bedroom. Mrs. Duart turned to go downstairs.

But in the doorway she was stopped by her husband. "Mary, come back in. I've got to speak to you."

"No. Come in here. Ian's sleeping." She led the way into the room got ready for James Mennock and shut the door. In the firelight, the only light in the room, she could see that her husband seemed worried. "Well, Hector? Quick. I can't leave a guest without a welcome."

"There's two, Mary. I thought you should be warned."

"Two?"

"He's brought a young woman with him."

Instinctively, Mary Duart turned to see what she looked like, however dimly, in the guest room mirror. "Young woman? What young woman?"

"A Miss Gailes. They're engaged to be married and have come to ask me to marry them."

"Well, that's very nice, Hector. You'll be glad to do that when the time comes, I daresay. And there's plenty to eat for their supper. What's bothering you then?"

"I don't know, Mary. It's kinna queer."

"Queer?"

"They've come with a bag each."

"To *stay*, Hector?"

"It looks like it."

"They can't! How can they? They'll have friends here about, they'll be going to. Have they said nothing?"

The minister of West Hyde shook his head.

Mary Duart stood arguing with herself. Rightly or wrongly, she saw Doctor Mennock as the young man who had given her husband back to her little more than a year ago. Thus her prejudice ran strong in the doctor's favor; although, indeed, her conventionality had thought it odd that after months of silence he should today have suddenly announced his coming without even making sure he would find them here. Still, that was nothing. And a single man was always an easy creature to provide for. But now a young woman too! And expecting to stay here! The mistress of the manse did not like these new-fangled liberties to be taken with her own or her husband's dignity. She had not somehow imagined the doctor to be one who would allow himself to do such things. But then she had known him so little, though Hector thought worlds of him. Of course Hector, so quick to see in some directions, could be so blind in others! Still, there had been those weeks of dread in Glasgow. And Hector had always said it was nobody but Doctor Mennock who had—

"What are you standing there thinking, Mary?"

"I was just thinking I would have to make up the single bed in the wee room that's good enough for the divinity students when they come to take a preaching for you, Hector. And wondering if it would be good enough for the doctor. This here will have to be given to the young lady." Mrs. Duart stood, her mind made up; herself now ready to dispense hospitality, come what might. She must not allow a strange invasion like this to knock her off her balance. "Come away, Hector," she said, laying a firm hand upon the arm of her anxious husband. "Or the poor things will be thinking the parish manse of West Hyde has lost its mistress!"

IV

It was a buxom, well-favored woman, still under thirty and in full command of herself, who came into her pleasant country drawing room some minutes later. Herself a reassuring sight for Charlotte, Mrs. Duart was in her own turn reassured by the appearance of the girl whose hand she had just taken. The doctor's companion was, whatever the reason for their coming, neither bold nor underbred. This handsome child's distinction made itself at once apparent. But it was such a young distinction, such a bewildered, lost distinction, that the elder woman was ready to be touched.

"So you're to be the wife of our friend the doctor, Miss— Gailes, is it? We're very glad to see you! And Hector's to be asked to marry you, I hear? Well, we count that an honor, don't we? After what the doctor did for us. But like enough, the doctor would never tell you a word about that! Did you now, Doctor?" She wondered at James's solemnity as she turned to greet him too.

"Doctor Mennock! You're not 'fashed' at me for saying that, are you?"

"No, no, Mrs. Duart." Here James stopped, uncertain, to look at her husband. "But—well—I've something very serious to say to you, Mr. Duart, and it must be said at once."

Hector Duart turned to James, suddenly nervous. "I'd be glad to be of service to you, Doctor Mennock," he said, seeking support in formal speech.

But as James opened his mouth to speak, Mrs. Duart stopped him. "Is it anything you couldn't be saying to Hector alone? This girl here is tired with her journey, wherever you've come from— Glasgow, is it?—and I would like to look after her. I have a fire in the good room to take her to."

"Yes. Take Charlotte, Mrs. Duart. It's very kind of you."

"Well, Doctor?" Now on the hearthrug before the fire, holding the lapels of his black coat and setting his legs apart, Hector Duart had unconsciously fallen into his attitude for professional listening. His lean, white face was intent.

"We want you to marry us, Mr. Duart."

The minister's voice sounded less troubled than the minister felt as he answered: "Yes, so you've said, Doctor. And you know how well pleased I am about that."

"Yes, Mr. Duart. But we want you to marry us tonight. Now! At once!"

So that was it? Clutching his coat the other man's dark eyes began looking about the room; looking everywhere but into James Mennock's; looking for resolution to tell this young man, to whom he owed so much, what he knew he must tell him.

James waited.

"What kind of certificate have you got, Doctor Mennock?" Hector Duart said at last.

"No certificate whatever. But—"

"I was feart o' that."

But to the minister's relief the door opened, readmitting his wife. "Can I come in? I've left her to come down when she's ready. Or do you want me to go away?"

"No. Come in, Mary."

She looked from troubled face to troubled face.

"Doctor Mennock wants to be married to Miss Gailes tonight, Mary. But he says he has no kind of certificate."

"But surely there can be a religious marriage!" James interposed. "Mr. Duart, there has got to be a marriage! That's why I brought Charlotte here to you, as the only man who could help us! Oh, there's no child coming! It's not that. But a marriage there has got to be! For you see—you see we can't go on as we are!" James's voice had broken. He stopped, sat down, and bending forward, ran a desperate hand across his eyes and through his tumbled hair.

Mary Duart looked at him with surprise. This was indeed an odd affair. She was glad she had come in to help Hector with it.

"Draw forward your chair to the fire, Doctor. See, I'll sit here. Sit down, Hector, and let the doctor tell us all about it."

And so, in stumbling, anxious words, the broken sincerity of which added to their pleading, the story of James and Charlotte was quickly told. Its different stages; the refusals, frustrations and affronts that had led them to this house. How, daring greatly but with Charlotte's fixed consent, he had brought her here. How he was determined to meet her parents' blunt No by a step—a ceremony that was irrevocable. In this increasing excitement, James got up and paced the room. What was to happen, he demanded hotly, if that ceremony be now denied them? Didn't the Duarts know what kind of a man he, James Mennock, was? And couldn't they see for themselves what kind of child this was he had brought with him? Did they expect him to compromise her? To take seedy possession of her like a cheap seducer?

The minister of West Hyde and his wife did not indeed expect James to do anything of the kind. Nor would they, had they been given all the time in the world to think about it. They were earnest young people, serving their Maker unsuspiciously and simply according to their own, very far from inconsiderable lights. Their good will neither sought nor found entertainment in the reports of evil, and they only obliged themselves to deal with it in pity when they found it—as often enough they must—lying awkward and unavoidable across their path.

But Hector Duart could see no evil here. Rashness, impatience, passion-ruled decisions and judgments. Hurt and a great distress brought to the door of Charlotte's blindly protective parents. Perhaps all these. But no. Not evil. Yet all this did not change the law of Scotland. And although to Hector Duart, indeed, religious marriage must ever count above legal marriage, the law would not oblige by seeing marriage through Hector Duart's eyes.

"My wife and I think nothing but good of you and the young lady, James," he said, breaking, in his earnestness, the diffidence that Scots of that time felt over the use of Christian names. "And I would marry you if I could this very night. But did you not know that under the law that wouldna be a marriage? And that I myself would be liable to suffer penalties?"

"Hector!"

"It's true, Mary. A minister has to know these things."

The room turned silent with unhappiness. Then Mary Duart spoke: "Is there no other way?"

"Irregular ways. Ways that are ways in the sight of the law. Ways that have nothing to do with me, a minister of the Kirk."

"But what kind of ways, Hector? Tell us."

V

Once more the handle turned and Charlotte stood in the doorway. Her outdoor things were thrown aside and she had set herself to rights with an almost schoolgirl haste. For a time she remained there hesitating, looking at the others, wondering what to do. And yet, as she waited, wide-eyed and uncertain, the bearing of this tall young girl with her fine dark hair and with the color back in her cheeks somehow proclaimed to those more simple people the distinction of her background: her pride, the metal she was made of. It was a bearing that imposed itself, despite her natural qualities of gentleness.

Hector Duart rose to his feet. The young man who had brought her here crossed to take her hand and to close the door behind her. It was on Mary Duart's tongue to rewelcome her, bidding her to come over to the fire, but James, standing beside her and still holding her hand, took the first word.

"Charlotte, we've met some trouble."

"For you and me, James? About our marriage?"

"Aye."

Mrs. Duart, watching, saw Charlotte's eyelids flicker, then saw too how at once, instinctively, a quickly summoned poise imposed control.

"Well, James?"

"I've told our friends here all there is to tell about us, Charlotte. They understand. But it seems the law of Scotland won't allow Mr. Duart to marry us without a proper certificate."

The girl's face flamed and her lip trembled, forcing her to bite it. But she merely stood waiting until she could trust herself to speak. "Then what are we to do, James? We can't go back to Glasgow. Father and Mother—" there was a halt here but at once she went on: "Father and Mother mustn't see us again until we've been married somehow."

"Mr. Duart was just telling us there was another way, when you came in," his wife hastened to say consolingly. She was touched by the sight of this proud girl and how she was meeting her dilemma. "What was it you were saying, Hector?"

The minister too was meeting a dilemma. His conscience was torn. Why had he let that word "irregular" escape from his lips just now? Was it for a man of his cloth to explain to these young people that in Scotland there was still an irregular form of marriage, unrecognized by their church, but yet a marriage by law? He could not think so. And yet? What if he did not? Might it not, after all, be forcing these two along a path they did not want to take? Or if principle refused to let them take it, then back to their separate homes, to misunderstanding and heartbreak? What right had he, Hector Duart, who owed this fine young man so much, to force such a choice upon him?

His wife, guessing his struggle, got up from her chair and laid her hand upon his sleeve. "Well, Hector?" Her voice was quiet. "I think that you should tell us."

And so, earnestly, Hector Duart told them. But not before he had appealed hurriedly and mutely for guidance. "There's a quick irregular marriage, but one that's legal. One that canna be put asunder. I don't know how it works. But it exists, that I know."

James turned to the girl whose hand he still held.

"Could you accept that kind of marriage, Charlotte?"

For a time she did not speak. He felt her fingers tighten in his own. "We have to be married at once, James, don't we? It's all that we can do."

To break solemnity, Mrs. Duart became brisk and bustling. "There we are, then." She patted her husband's shoulder. "You did quite right to tell them. And now I'll need to go and see about—"

"That's all very well, Mary, but—" The minister's eyes were large with trouble.

"No. It was the right thing to do, Hector!" His wife cut him short now, yet she knew well that at a later time and in private she would be called upon to help her man to wrestle with his devils of uncertainty. "A lawyer in Dumfries would tell the doctor all he needs to know, wouldn't he?" she went on. "We could give him the name of ours."

"I would like my name kept out of this, James. It's not for myself but for the Kirk's sake. Can you understand that?"

James understood. Hospital experience of Hector Duart had taught him that the minister of West Hyde was no moral coward. "That's all right. I'll get this information for myself. If you can keep Charlotte, Mrs. Duart, I'll get back to Dumfries tonight, in some way. Isn't there a hotel at the station? I can find out about this, first thing in the morning, and come back here."

"Of course we'll keep Miss Gailes here, Doctor! Where else could she go, would you tell me? And Hector will lend you the horse and rig. And now I'll go and hurry up the supper. You'll both be starving? You can stay with us for a wee while after it, Doctor. But I would advise you to start for Dumfries very soon. What with having to drive a strange horse and not knowing your way. Hector can have the reading early tonight and that will let you get off."

And so, some two hours later, James and Charlotte rose from their knees at the conclusion of the reading that was a part of the manse's evening routine; bade each other good night outside in the darkness; then James drove back to Dumfries. And thus they were parted until the morning.

It was an unexpected finish to this, the day of their elopement.

VI

James came back from Dumfries rather sooner than they had ex-

[201]

pected him. It was a little past midmorning when the wheels of the gig made themselves heard.

Determination and a sense of great urgency had forced him to act quickly. On his arrival at the station hotel in the late evening he had received the name of a legal firm at the reception desk. In the morning he was on the firm's doorstep, waiting for the door to open. A sharp clerk with more push than authority found for him the information he needed, looking to win praise for his initiative in so doing from his employers when they should arrive presently and advising James to wait and no doubt witness the bestowal of that praise. But James had merely left his address that payment could, in course, be asked of him, and hurried off at once.

He found Charlotte on the lawn in front of the manse trying to control the third member of the Duart family, whose uncertain feet were treading down a clump of yellow crocuses, while his fat hands were trying to pick them and to thrust them into his mouth.

"Oh, you're there, Doctor? We hardly expected you so early. Did you see a lawyer and get what you wanted? Here! What do you think *you're* doing?" Mrs. Duart, who had come from the house on hearing the gig, swept down upon her son, caught him up and set him on her knee. "Come and sit beside me, Charlotte," she called, indicating a place on the garden seat beside her.

The warmth implied in Mary Duart's use of Charlotte's name pleased James as now he turned to thank the minister's man who had come to take the horse's head.

"Yes. I've got what I needed." James looked at Charlotte uneasily. "It seems to me a queer way of doing things. But it's a marriage. I made quite sure about that. Irregular but legal."

"What did they say, James?"

James took a memorandum from his pocket. "The young man at the lawyer's wrote this out for me." He began to read:

Irregular Marriage. Declaration de praesenti. If a man and woman mutually declare that they accept each other as husband and wife, this constitutes in Scotland a valid marriage. It is not sufficient to promise to marry in the future: there has to be an interchange of consent to present marriage. If it can be proved that the man has said: "I take you, A. B. for my wife," or points to her before witnesses and says: "This is my wife," and she signifies her agreement, there is a good marriage.

[202]

It is also possible to constitute marriage in this way when one party gives the other a written declaration or acknowledgment that they are man and wife and this is accepted by the other.

If the fact of marriage is disputed, however, the conduct at the time of the alleged marriage is also examined to enable the court to determine whether, in fact, there has been true consent.

"I'm not sure that I understand all that," Charlotte said. "May I see it?" She took the note from James's hand.

Mary Duart's eyes looked up at the worried face of the tall young man standing there in front of her. Then they moved to the girl who sat at her side, bending tense and tremulous to read what he had given her. From these they turned to scan the lawn lying moist and sparkling in the light of the March morning; then on beyond across the fields to a gleaming line of sunshine on the distant Solway Firth; then further still to faraway England where phantom clouds touched the phantom peaks of Lakeland.

Her heart was sorry for these two. This did not seem a proper marriage to herself any more than it appeared to be to them. Yet the doctor had made sure of its legality. And she knew they must be married.

"Does this mean that we need witnesses?" Charlotte was asking.

"Mr. Duart was called to the village," his wife said apologetically and not quite relevantly. "He didn't expect the doctor back so soon." It occurred to her that her husband might have run away, but at once she dismissed the unworthy thought.

"No," James answered. "I can write a statement and we'll both sign it. Later we'll put it somewhere safe and show it to anybody that wants to see it. This extract says that will do. I know Mr. Duart doesna like this, so I'm asking none of the folk here to be witnesses. Come with me, Charlotte. I'll write it now and we'll sign." He held out his hand to lead her inside.

Mrs. Duart put the little boy down. Knowing her husband's scruples, she was pleased that James should make no difficulty either for the minister or for herself. "If I'm not to be a witness," she said illogically, "surely you'll let Ian and me come in to see what you're doing."

And so at Hector Duart's desk, James sat down to write the following:

[203]

West Hyde, Dumfriesshire. March 12, 1903.

This day, I, James Bruce Mennock, bachelor, declare that I have taken Charlotte Mackinnon Gailes, spinster, to be my wife according to the law of Scotland. And I, Charlotte Mackinnon Gailes, declare that this day I have acknowledged James Bruce Mennock to be my husband.

This James read aloud, then set his name to it. Thereafter he rose from the desk to make way for Charlotte who sat down and set her name beneath his own.

And now, as she watched them, it came to the mistress of the manse that beneath a show of calmness these two were much shaken by what they did; shaken by the knowledge that they were passing an important milestone. She was not surprised to see that, as she stood up from signing, Charlotte's face was flushed and that her eyes were large with tears. Nor was she surprised that James should bend to kiss Charlotte gently with a kiss that seemed in itself a consecration. "Doctor and Mrs. James Mennock," Mary Duart whispered, awestruck, herself caught into this long moment of solemnity. "The Minister has some wine," she said at last, judging the moment past. "When he comes we'll drink your health."

"I'm here, Mary."

"Hector! We didn't hear you! Do you see what has happened? They're married according to the law of Scotland."

"According to the law."

"Hector—" his wife paused, daring greatly, "Hector, you couldn't ask for a blessing on them, could you?"

Mr. Duart did not answer quite at once. He stood with his eyes on the floor searching once more, as his wife well knew, for the way he ought to take. But at length he raised them, joined his hands and looked towards James and Charlotte. "Surely I can pray," he said, "for the future happiness of my friends."

This then was the marriage of James and Charlotte Mennock. And so they were ever to regard it. Any ceremony that followed would be to them a mere form; a thing of small significance performed to please others.

CHAPTER EIGHTEEN

I

And another ceremony did follow. In the Lakeland town of Keswick one morning in early April. A warm, damp morning of green promise with a white cloud blanketing the summit of Skiddaw and with the mists rising slowly in shifting, thinning veils from the still surface of Derwentwater and from the budding woods along its shores; rising to reveal, as the sun dispersed them, the wet rich flanks of the Cat Bells hillside, the luminous, rounded cones beyond the Newlands Valley, and then presently, at the lake's further end, the broken, Chinese beauty of the crags in the Jaws of Borrowdale.

It had been James's first intention to bring Charlotte back with him to Kinaldie at once. But now, as a result of their irregular marriage, he had felt this would not do. They must find a place where they might spend some time together like any other newly married couple, giving evidence that so indeed they regarded themselves; evidence that could, if need be, provide easy confirmation later. Mary Duart gave him an address in Keswick where, not so many years since, she and her reverend bridegroom had spent their own short honeymoon. It was here on their third day of flight that Charlotte's father found them.

Returning home from Edinburgh, the professor and his wife were faced with a night of panic. Where was Miss Charlotte? None of the servants knew. Lunch had been got ready, but she had not appeared to eat it. They had decided she had gone out forgetting to tell them. Yes. They had heard some movement during midmorning and what might have been the voice of a man. But they had concluded that Miss Charlotte, seeing the postman or someone else from a window, had merely gone, as she often did, to open the front door herself.

"The voice of a man, Edie?" The professor turned to his wife after the servants were dismissed. "You don't think that Mennock—?"

"I've been thinking that all the time, Henry." She noticed the hand her husband had put forth to grasp the back of a chair was trembling.

If Henry were threatening to go to pieces she must, whatever it cost, hold herself together.

"Edie? What are we to do?"

"I'll go up and search her room. No. First I'll look at the trunks." As she went upstairs Edith felt a sense of nausea. Yes. A familiar handbag was missing from the storeroom. It had been there this morning. She could remember moving it aside to get at the dressing case she was taking to Edinburgh. Charlotte's room. It had been prepared for the night by a servant, with the bed made ready and the child's night things laid out as usual. But Edith knew her daughter's clothes. It took no time for her to make sure that certain things were missing.

"Edie!" the professor had puffed upstairs behind her.

"She has packed a bag and gone, Henry."

"What? She can't! We must telephone round her friends!"

"No. It's late. And we can't have any talk. I'm certain it's Doctor Mennock."

"Edie—I don't—I don't know what to do!"

"Go downstairs and pour yourself out some whisky, Henry. I'm going to telephone those Lyndoch people."

But neither Walter nor Bertha Lyndoch knew anything. They were all earnest concern and they promised all their help. They would have spoken at once to the young doctor's house at Kinaldie, Walter said, but his dead brother-in-law had been old-fashioned in his ways and his son had not yet been able to have a telephone put in. Charlotte's father at once decided to take an early morning train.

But the behavior of James Mennock's stepmother had been quite unlike her sister's. The strange, thin woman had sat there, stiff and angrily defensive in her black dress, primly and coldly telling the poor professor nothing. Had Doctor Mennock been away from Kinaldie? He was often away from Kinaldie. But during the past night? He often stayed overnight at outlying farms if there was serious illness. But had he packed a bag? He always took his doctor's bag. But a bag containing personal things? How could she tell what was in his bag?

Thus, after her fashion did Constance Mennock stand bewildered but determined behind her husband's son, knowing nothing but loyally covering his tracks. A stubborn, dismaying performance, which the generous professor was laughingly to recount to his son-in-law sometime later.

On his return home in the early afternoon, however, Edith met
him with a telegram in her hand.

WAS MARRIED TO JAMES MENNOCK THIS MORNING.

CHARLOTTE

It had been handed in at Dumfries.
And thus they found them. Dumfries. West Hyde. Keswick.

II

The sun was fully out now, as they came from the Presbyterian
chapel that had in courtesy lent its walls for a marriage in England
by a minister of the Church of Scotland. At James's summons Hector
Duart, with no refusal this time, had, accompanied by his wife,
crossed the border to perform the ceremony.

It was a strange uneasy wedding party that stood there at the
chapel door dazed a little by the April sunshine. There were smiles
and tears, of course. But it would take a long time to reconcile the
irreconcilable.

For Edith these had been bitter anxious weeks. Her husband, making for the address that the greatly troubled minister of West Hyde
parish had felt in duty bound to give him, had run into the young
couple, jauntily arm-in-arm, returning from the photographer's. He
had brought them back to his hotel.

What had happened between Charlotte and her mother, Charlotte's husband had never really known. His wife, it seemed, could
never bear to speak of it. He and the professor had sat together
waiting, passing the time in an ecstasy of awkward small talk and
still more awkward silence. But the meeting in Edith's room had,
James knew, been stormy.

Back in their lodgings once more, Charlotte had thrown herself
upon him; weeping her heart out and crying that she had wanted
to hurt nobody, least of all her own mother; demanding how she
could ever be expected to leave him; and asking hysterically and
with a passion that was largely rhetorical, as James rightly guessed,
what she was to do?

She was to calm herself and be a good girl, her husband had said,
displaying a new and salutary firmness. And hadn't she better tell
him just what her mother had said that he might better help?

No. Charlotte had never quite done this. That meeting with her mother had ever remained raw in his wife's sensibilities. And very soon James saw that it was best not to try to speak of it.

But later talks with the professor, arrangements to be made, told James enough. Edith did not consider her daughter married. Charlotte had flared up at this as an insult to her husband. James could not be dishonorable even if he tried! They had done everything legally necessary. And besides the minister of West Hyde had prayed over them! Very well. Would Charlotte consent to remarriage? If James consented too. And meantime, hadn't she better come to the hotel to be with her parents until this marriage could take place? Never! They were fully man and wife now. It would be the greatest wickedness for her parents to separate them!

And so the professor and his wife had been forced to withdraw, defeated, leaving their daughter in Keswick, and receiving the young man's promise that he would make the soonest possible arrangements. It was better, they decided, that everything, all preliminaries and the marriage itself, should take place here where the name of Mackinnon Gailes meant nothing and where tongues would find little profit in wagging.

James, pliable and humble now that he had won, was pleased to agree to everything. The time of waiting necessary to legal marriage in England would be their honeymoon. He would write letters home and do all that was needed here.

And Charlotte? For the rest of that day she had continued unhappy and at times there were tears. But high spirits and Charlotte could not long remain apart. Next morning there were signs of recovery. And by the morning following that, she was demanding of her husband if any girl had ever had so happy a honeymoon as she was having? To which James, still getting to know his wife and still marveling at her volatility, replied that he was not quite in a position to say. And wouldn't it have been awful if their marriage had not been an adventure like this, but a silly humdrum affair like everybody else's? Silly humdrum affairs, her husband felt obliged to point out, could in their way be less of a strain.

But now, here at the chapel door with the irregular made regular, James knew these days of foolish happiness were ended. Now he must show himself responsible. Now he must make his peace. As yet he had scarcely exchanged a word with Charlotte's mother. "I would like to be friends with you," he said simply.

Edith's own hand trembled as it clasped the long fingers of her daughter's husband. She stood holding them for a moment, looking away, saying nothing, giving herself time perhaps to conquer what she felt. But at last she turned back to look him in the eyes and speak. "James, I have been thinking of what to say to you. We must be quite honest with each other. I dislike this marriage. And I dislike you for bringing it about. But this is the last time anyone will ever hear me say so. For Charlotte's sake I shall do everything to try to like you. I hope you will try to do the same for me."

"I'll do all I can, Mrs. Gailes." Her words seemed cold to him. Yet her honesty spoke to his own. They were never to become close friends, these two, but they would remain loyal enough allies. The family ranks had closed.

A fresh breeze sprang up. A sudden breeze with ice in it blowing down from lingering snowdrifts up there in the high places. The wedding guests caught at their hats and drew their coats and wraps about them. Then, deciding it was foolish to linger, turned from the chapel door and set off briskly in the sparkling April sunshine.

CHAPTER NINETEEN

I

Lady Mennock appeared in her husband's study-bedroom. "James! Why are you not in bed?"

It was very late, but not yet quite dark, since it was May.

Sir James looked up from his fireside chair. "I'm waiting to see Maggs safely back."

"You could wait perfectly well in bed. Come along, Macpherson. It's high time you were in your bed too." She caught up the white terrier from his knee and stood holding the little creature in her arms.

"I'm waiting here where I am."

"But that's ridiculous, James! Doctor Struan's airplane was coming from Europe. It's sure to be hours late. Airplanes always are."

The old man half laughed, half grunted. "Charlotte," he said, "you were always a terrible body for making statements."

When she had left him he lay back, crossed one hand over the other and returned to the train of thought from which he had been roused.

His granddaughter and young Struan. What, in those last months, had they been up to? They seemed very good friends. Any of these days he had expected to be told they had decided to marry. Well, he had no objections. Or if he had, they were such objections as he must keep to himself. He did not want to lose Margaret again. That was all they came to. An old man's selfishness.

Sir James did not believe in close but platonic friendships between muscular giants of thirty and attractive young women of twenty-six or -seven. Sooner or later there must come an emotional explosion, even though the giant in question were afflicted by a paralyzing shyness. What then had been happening?

But now this very night Joe was off to Canada with Margaret driving him and his luggage to Prestwick aerodrome as though she were his sister! No. These modern young people were quite incomprehensible. Didn't they know their own minds?

Now in his young days— Sir James's thinking brought him to the sheets lying there on the table beside him, these last chapters of Margaret's narrative. Well? Hadn't he known his own mind about Charlotte? And hadn't she, young as she was, known hers about him? Now that had been an emotional explosion! An explosion that had gone off with violence, blowing parental resistance aside and, too, blowing himself along the road of his destiny. A short while with his young wife in Kinaldie. Then Glasgow again with Mackinnon Gailes helping this time. The climbing of the ladder.

And then, of course, Sandy. His deep love for his young son. His pride in the little boy with gay ways and a personal beauty such as he, the country lad from Kinaldie, had never known. His fading hopes as Sandy grew up. The years of unhappiness. The agony of the end.

Sir James rose slowly, pulling himself up by the arm of his chair and fumbling for his stick. He crossed to the drawer in his desk where he had locked the telltale diary and took it out. Now standing before the fire, he turned the pages. The end of October, 1930. There were no entries for several days. His mind had not been on diary writing. He turned a page. Yes. This was it. The record of a happening that had come near to breaking his heart.

Today Sandy and Grace were buried. The coffins were taken direct to the cemetery from last night's train; the train we all came home in. We being Sandy's child, the nurse I had got to travel with her and myself. There was a short service by the graveside. Mrs. Gailes stayed at home with Charlotte. There will be an announcement in tomorrow's newspaper. That will be all. Now my boy and his wife are lying beside his grandfather, the old professor, out there in the Western Necropolis.

Charlotte is in bed. Her mother is beside her. I have come down here to be alone. Old habit has made me reach for the consolation of this diary.

Yet what can I write that can give me any consolation? My son is dead, because I, his own father, refused the help that would have saved him. No. I cannot write about this.

But I will try to put down the bare facts.

A police inspector came to my consulting room four mornings

ago. London had just telephoned to say that Sandy and Grace had been found shot. I went at once to Charlotte's mother. The old lady was good. She kept herself well in hand and told me I had done right to come to her first. She helped me to get to the afternoon train without seeing the boy's mother. She thought that best. She had decided to tell Charlotte in the first place that I had got a sudden call south because they were both very seriously ill. We arranged I was to telephone to my poor wife from London that night saying that the young couple had died of influenza within a few hours of each other. This is what Charlotte still believes.

Another inspector met me in London and took me to Sandy's lodgings. The bodies were still there, laid out on the bed in a shabby Soho room kept by an Italian woman. A young policeman was in charge. I was allowed to examine them. The girl had been shot in the back of the head. Sandy was shot in the temple. The contents of his pocket and other things were laid out on a table. Old letters and suchlike. A moneylender's demand and, God forgive me, my own letter received on the morning he shot himself. The story is clear enough.

My son was in the hands of a moneylender who had bullied him into writing to me. That letter of Sandy's had told me the truth, though I didn't believe it. I took it as a new way of getting money out of me. He had never, to my knowledge, been in the hands of a moneylender before. My fatal temper did the rest. I wrote him I was having nothing more to do with him or his. That finished it! He went out in the morning after he got it, it would seem. Round midday he came back raving. He had drunk himself out of his senses. The Italian woman heard him going upstairs, heard the door bang, heard the girl's cry, then a shot. The woman shouted to ask what was wrong and tried to force the door. She is a strong, heavy woman and the door gave way. Grace was on the floor face down and my poor, demented boy had turned the pistol towards his daughter, who had been hurriedly thrown down on the bed. The Italian struck the pistol aside, but not out of his hand, and made to pick up the baby. While she was doing this there was another shot and she turned. Sandy had killed himself. The woman ran for a policeman carrying the child in her arms.

And all this because of my letter! No! I will go back upstairs to Charlotte.

Sir James raised his eyes and looked about him stupidly. How long ago was it since he had forced himself to read these pages? Forced himself to see that room with its window curtain of torn net, its greasy wallpaper and those sheeted figures on the bed? Now, after so many years the picture again stood before him, vivid in its detail. Now after so many years he could see the officer who had brought him, the young policeman and the buxom Italian woman who had saved his granddaughter's life.

But now there was another figure. The lean figure of a man, still in his early fifties, standing there among them, bewildered and broken with self-reproach. To his surprise, James Mennock felt sorry for this figure of his younger self. Maybe, after all, his son would have been too much for any father. Maybe he had been wrong to blame himself so bitterly. He had, in the main, done his best with the impossible. If disaster had not happened then, it would inevitably have happened later. Would there ever have been hope for such as Sandy?

The long fingers trembled as he turned a page.

Glad to find Charlotte making an effort. Neither of us slept much. But in spite of that she insisted on getting up to see that everything was all right with her granddaughter. This should be the saving of her. She had been beginning to ask me questions, but I overheard her mother telling her to leave me alone meantime.

I must say old Mrs. Gailes is doing well. The woman is made of grand stuff. She is a great strength to us at this time. I wish I could like her better. I find she has already taken the servants into her confidence and telephoned several friends to make sure that all this will be kept from Charlotte. The maids have even been told to watch newspapers coming into the house. If there is anything about Sandy, the newspaper sheet is to go amissing. But I don't think there will be much. All the London authorities were kind and understood that a press sensation about a professor's son shooting his wife and himself must for all our sakes be avoided. Here in Glasgow the responsible press will do what it can. Besides, anybody that reads anything will not, surely, be so tactless, so coarse, as to speak of it before the boy's mother.

And so it had been. At first there had been fears and sudden alarms. But the ring of protective silence that everyone's affection and Charlotte's own transparent trustfulness had put about her had in the end stood unbroken. Her gentleness had been kept from a shock it had better never have.

No. She had never known how Sandy died. Nor that he, Sandy's father, had written that letter. He had decided it must be a secret punishment for himself alone. A heavy burden that must weigh upon him for the rest of his days.

And had it? The old man closed the diary and stood looking into the fire. No. Life with its consolations had closed in again. Pleasant everyday happenings. Daily routine. The little girl growing up in the house. His joy in the mastery of his profession. His friends. His success. And Charlotte. Always there. A being so different from himself, yet so much a part of him now, that he had no measure with which to gauge his love of her. Was he shallow, light-minded, trivial, that for many years grief and self-condemnation had lost their power to sting him? At the end of his life James Mennock could not think so. Perhaps it was not in the flesh to endure sorrow, undiminished and continuing. Or perhaps it was that, despite all, God had decided to forgive him.

And Margaret? She had told him she was writing no more of the family story. He had agreed with her that she had written quite enough. That she had better try her hand at something new, something of her own. Besides, his papers would lead her to the story of her father now. No. She had better leave all that alone.

Sir James turned round and, taking his ebony stick, prodded a lump of coal until it splintered and flamed up, then he bent forward, opened the diary wide that its pages might burn the more quickly and placed it on the blaze. As he stood watching, he heard his grand-daughter's key in the outside door.

II

Would Margaret wonder what he was burning? Hastily he stirred the half-consumed pages, then turned back and stood in front of them, screening the blaze with his legs.

But she noticed nothing. She had opened the door quietly, fearing he might already be asleep. "Grandfather! Not in bed?"

"I was waiting up for you. Did Joe get the plane all right?"

"It was down when we got to Prestwick. But he had plenty of time. They flew at ten."

[214]

He watched her with curiosity as she flung herself into his chair, lay back and looked up at him. Was she in some kind of agitation? Excitement? Had there been tears? "Ten? And it's getting on for twelve? Where have you been?"

"Nowhere. Driving back."

"Two hours from Prestwick with the roads clear? Trouble with the car?"

She shook her head. She could not tell him she had halted by the roadside more than once, put her head in her hands and given way to feelings to which she herself could not yet put a name. The loss of a friend? Joe's behavior at the airport? While the sweetness of the green Ayrshire evening, the settling mist, the heavy perfume of the May had come to her through the car's open windows; calling to her refound youth, disturbing still more her already disturbed heart.

The old man stretched out a hand, begging for her confidence. "Maggs? What's wrong, then? I can see there's something."

She sat up, caught it, touched the back of it with her lips and let it fall again. "Joe Struan asked me to marry him tonight."

"So that's it, is it?" Sir James smiled. "He chose a queer time."

"He asked me just as we were saying goodbye."

"He might have done it earlier."

"Yes." But again she could not speak of how the paragon's offer had come about. How in the hurly-burly of the great air station and just at the last moment, when the transatlantic passengers had been called and people were collecting coats and bags and exchanging goodbyes, the great, foolish creature's feelings had at last burst through his shyness. How, wringing the blood from the hand she had given him and with tears emerging from behind the thick lenses, he had asked her to follow him to Canada and become his wife.

"I've been expecting him to ask you for months," her grandfather was saying.

Margaret did not reply. But now she knew she had been expecting it too.

"And what was your answer, Maggs?"

She shrugged. "How could there be any immediate answer? I could only promise him faithfully I would cable him the moment I knew my own mind."

For a time neither spoke. Behind Sir James, as he stood meditating before the fire, the pages of the diary turned to grey, floating ashes.

"You were good friends," he said presently. "I've been watching you. And you didna seem to want anybody else last winter."

"I was busy and he happened to be about."

"It wasna just that."

She did not contradict this. "I would hate to leave you and Grandmother," she said.

He turned an amused smile upon her. "That's something new. It took me all my time to keep you here in the autumn."

"Canada is so far away!"

"We'll send you an airplane ticket if we want you." These were mere, nervous arguments he saw. Arguments inviting contradiction.

"And there's Donald. Wouldn't it be unfair to Donald's memory?"

"Did Donald ever say he didna want you to live your life?"

"No."

"Very well, then. *He's* not here to give it to you. So where would be the unfairness? If you've found another man who can mean something to you—and you havena told me yet that Joe means nothing —take him and get on with it."

She stood up abruptly and began pacing the room as he continued talking.

"Oh, it'll always be easy enough for you to get another man, if you want one. *Some* kinna man. You've only to look at yourself in the looking glass. But there are not many with the stuff in them that Joe Struan has. I'll write him a certificate if you like. Oh, he's shy and queer. And he needs a smart lassie like you to stand beside him and build him up. But you can take it from me the job will be worth doing! Well?"

She had turned round on her heel and was waiting to speak. "Grandfather, *is* it really worth it?"

"Worth it? Have I not just been telling you?"

"You spoke of Donald wanting me to live my life just now."

"Oh, you'll live some kinna life whether you want or not. Unless somebody drops a bomb on your head. But—"

"No, Grandfather! Listen! I was a young girl when I married Donald. I only knew that I adored him. That was enough for me then. I didn't think further. Now it's different. Quite different. If I married Joe Struan I would be doing it with the knowledge and feelings of a grown woman. I had better tell you, I suppose, that on the way home, I stopped the car and cried at the thought of Joe being on one side of the Atlantic and myself on the other. But I know now that existence is not all a young girl's honeymoon. I know that from my own experience. Yes, and from what I've come to know of yours and Granny's."

"Of course! But—"

"For instance, if you'll let me speak of him for once, there was my father. Poor Granny has told me. The misery. The hopelessness. Would you dare to face all that again? Is it worth—worth baring our breasts to such things. Inviting the rough as well as the smooth?"

Her grandfather was standing with his head bowed, staring at the hearthrug. "It wasna all misery, Maggs," he said. "Do you think I got nothing out of having a son? Do you think I havena any memories of the wee boy that used to run about this house?"

She stood waiting, giving the old man time to raise his head and fix her with his eyes.

"Is it worth it? Of course it's worth it! Don't lose your nerve, Maggs! It's not like you! I see you don't hate Joe Struan. Very well then; whether it's going to be smooth or rough—"

Once again Lady Mennock appeared. "James! Not in bed *yet!* I thought I heard a quarrel going on. Or were you only having one of your eternal arguments? Don't either of you realize what o'clock it is? Child! Whoever are you trying to telephone at this time of night?"

But now, since Margaret was too occupied to answer, James and Charlotte could only stand together listening, while their granddaughter inquired of the night operator to whom at this hour she could dictate a transatlantic cable.